LET
ME KNOW
WHEN
YOU'RE
HOME

LET
ME KNOW
WHEN
YOU'RE
HOME

STORIES *of*
FEMALE FRIENDSHIP

First published in Great Britain in 2020 by Dear Damsels

Collection © Dear Damsels, 2020

Fourteen © E.V. Somerville, 2020
What's On Your Mind © Hannah Wright, 2020
An Open Letter to a Friend Forgotten © Jade Greene, 2020
Seating Arrangements © Sara Sherwood, 2020
Memories of Honey © Alice Godliman, 2020
Firecracker © Huma Qureshi, 2020
This Side of the Mersey © Hannah Simpson, 2020
Airports © Jonatha Kottler, 2020
Here's What I Meant When I Said That © Francesca Raine, 2020
Her Name Was Forte © Alexandra Burton, 2020
Vignettes of You and Me © Chloe Tomlinson, 2020
Looking Back © Rosie Dastgir, 2020
Selkie © Rebecca Cooney, 2020
These Streets Are Not Our Own © Kimberly Kay, 2020
Finding Out © Sallyanne Rock, 2020

1

We acknowledge the phrase 'female friendship' puts emphasis on sex rather
than gender. The subtitle of this collection is not intended to exclude anyone
who identifies as a woman from the experiences shared in this publication.
These are stories by women, for women.

ISBN: 978-1-5272-5424-4

Printed and bound in Great Britain by Clays Ltd, Elcograf S.p.A.

Dear Damsels
www.deardamsels.com

For our friends.

CONTENTS

EDITORS' LETTER

What does female friendship mean to you?

Over the years, we've read hundreds of pieces of writing that responded to this question. On the surface, these stories might have been tackling a different subject – they could have been about love, youth or heartbreak. Perhaps they were about new beginnings or something coming to an end. But if you took a closer look, so many of these stories were quietly celebrating something else: female friendship.

Eventually, we started thinking about how we could give this messy, multi-faceted topic all the space it needed and deserved – a way that would allow the relationships between women to take centre stage.

We started with a phrase we'd said to each other many times before, and went from there.

In *Let Me Know When You're Home*, fifteen women writers explore what female friendship means to them through fiction, non-fiction and poetry, digging deep into the complexities and nuances of these relationships. From the friendships gone astray, burning too brightly and too quickly, to those that, when challenged, only bound together more tightly. Here are stories about the near misses of friendship; the rifts and the homecomings; the sourness, the competitiveness, the forgiveness and the joy that comes from living your life in tandem with other women.

We hope that you enjoy this book. We hope that it both reflects and challenges your understanding of the relationships between women. Most of all, we hope that when you finish it, you go on to share your own story of what female friendship means to you.

Love,
Abby & Bridie

Co-founders of Dear Damsels,
Editors of *Let Me Know When You're Home*

'we
sort of
grew up
together...'

GROWING UP

FOURTEEN

E.V. SOMERVILLE

(Written for the birthday of my best friend, a poem for speaking aloud.)

Boys in bands
And
Other understandable magnetisms
That we could barely handle,
Dancing witch rituals, in our bedrooms; candle, candle,
Sunlight floods in unwelcome, mornings come and come,
To break and remake us
We're growing,
And undone.
Our bedrooms postered all over
With dreams and riots;
A healthy diet of boisterous aspiration and cold cynicism that,
Entwined with quiet doubts,

Boldly believes that the world
Is out there
For those who care enough to
Cut class to protest the Iraq war or
Get piercings –
Before we're caught by caring parents
Who dread the thought of
Teenage daughters wrought with holes that
Sieve them empty
When there's
So much world to hold
Within our stretch-marked skin
Growing so fast, still learning
To adapt
Quickly
As this glowing world demands of
Us
And hope
We last through the fuss,
The hysterical nights howling about GCSEs, petty family fights, and
such intense crushes
Then up early for school
Braiding our hair on the busses
Eavesdropping on the older kids over there
Pretending not to care
But not daring to admit
Such shitty envy to even our best friends,
Who were in the end
(and all along!)
More substantial

More thrilling, more powerful more
Formative and figurative and
freshly forged and fruitful
Than all the crappy 'cool kids' who
Had all the points but none of youth's joy
Too eager to
Grow up, grow serious, get the boys.
Maybe we were all
Crumby,
In one way or another, though?
Weren't we all freaked out
and fearless, feckless, fly-by-night sometimes?
I suppose there is unbeauty, sometimes
In the aches of fresh growth.
Though, in the throes of long summer holidays
Water fights and late-night video sleepovers we
Never needed to run for cover, just
Trusted each other,
Implicitly,
With the safekeeping of ourselves;
Rested upon each other and grew
Like tangled ivy through
The dark cracks of the awkward years,
through all the summers swimming
And riding bikes
And through the
Meaningless fights that
Defined us
as we forged our boundaries
To remind us to stand somewhere on things which

Weren't meaningless at all.
We *always* fall back together after the break
There's too much at stake
So we always make anew;
(No matter the distance, old friend)
No heart without a part kept safe for you.

WHAT'S ON YOUR MIND?

HANNAH WRIGHT

A cursor flashes in the text box. You can type whatever you like and it will send to everyone. 'Everyone' is everyone you know or perhaps 'everyone' is only a collection of strangers. It might be your colleagues or your best friends. It might just simply be *everyone*. Everyone you've ever known or could ever hope to know; gathered by the companies that store the information on a server somewhere and save it up for some future use.

So, what is on your mind?

Technology has been as much a part of my closest relationships as friendship bracelets and fallings out. It's gone from feeling new and exciting to a part of the everyday, much like the best friendships themselves. Gone are the days of drunkenly holding hands and boldly declaring friendship forever, and in its place is something smaller, more private, but certain; a nugget of love and acceptance that travels with you and helps you feel less alone.

I sent my first text message before we all had phones in our pockets. At the time, we had a family mobile phone – a chunky black Motorola with fat rubber buttons that would pop as you pressed them – and I didn't know what a text message was. Sally Robinson was my best friend: her home was my second home, her laugh was my favourite, and around her neck hung the other half of my heart-shaped necklace.

We had the Robinson-family mobile number stored in our phone's small memory and Sally made sure she was the one to have their phone to hand when we conducted our experiment. The phones themselves didn't feel that revolutionary; we could already phone each other on our landlines. But landlines could be listened to by gross older brothers (hers) and annoying little sisters (mine) and so we'd been looking for other ways in which to communicate. We'd tried using toy shop walkie-talkies but they wouldn't cover the distance between her house and mine; tin cans were out of the question for this same reason though it didn't stop us from discussing the logistics; and letters and postcards were all well and good but we weren't happy with spending all our pocket money on stamps. A text message seemed like the ultimate way to keep in touch.

I message received

HELLO. DID THIS
WORK? SALLY
XXX

That we could type out words to one another and they would somehow end up on a phone more than a mile away felt like a revelation. It would be a few years before we got our own mobiles and discovered the compulsive need to beat each other at Snake, but the excitement of receiving that text is a vivid memory.

We started using the internet at the end of primary school and created email accounts with absurd addresses. We played online games and sometimes ventured into chat rooms, only to be appalled and confused by some of the conversations.

From: lostmyangelwings@hotmail.com
RE: Neopets!!

Sally went to another school and despite all these different ways of keeping in touch, we somehow lost it anyway. Soon there were other friends to text, new people to ring and the dizzying new world of high school and all its terrifying older teenagers and social pressures to navigate. We'd still sometimes go to the cinema on a Friday afternoon, but then she started to go to after-school activities or to new friends' houses and I had to settle into a new environment with a sharp pang of loss for something that was missing.

In the first few months of high school, relationships were cut-throat. New friendships bloomed and then were quickly pulled up by the roots when you were found to be less cool or too uptight or too weird. I would sometimes stay home from school, fever-wet with anxiety, dreading the moment that someone would offer me a cigarette or ask why I was already wearing a bra.

<3****Carrie!****<3 has just signed in

Tentatively new friendships that lasted beyond the first couple of weeks began to emerge. Though we saw each other most days, and had plenty of opportunities to talk in person, our friendships also existed online. Once we'd rushed home from school, bags dumped by the doorway, we'd sit down at our family computers and beg the use of the internet at the cost of no phone calls. We'd wait through the agonising digital chorus of the dial-up tone and the fear that perhaps today it wasn't working. We'd log on for really only one purpose: MSN Messenger. We could chat for hours, swapping song lyrics and sharing confidences. We talked to our closest friends and to those we didn't know so well. Whole friendships flourished on this platform, while during the day we would barely look at one another.

Sometimes you'd fall victim to being friendship catfished. You'd think you were chatting to one friend but actually there were three of them behind the screen and they asked pointed questions, most likely laughing at your answers.

NUDGE
NUDGE
NUDGE

We started to learn that there were downsides to these convenient communication methods, not least the worry about what would happen to your friendships if you couldn't log on for a night. And you started to realise that privacy was perhaps an issue, because although you were typing only for your closest friends' eyes, there was nothing stopping them from sharing these words with others if you had a fight or they decided their loyalty lay elsewhere.

Louise:
Did U tell Amy that I kissed Jack?

Soon after MSN, where we began cultivating our online identities, the first online network arrived to allow us to socialise more publicly. My friends and I were all quick to create MySpace accounts. We picked out profile pictures, typed our first bios, and learned how to personalise the colours of our pages and even the look of the cursor. But the real drama lay in the 'top 8': a list of your top friends, with links to their profiles.

Who you chose to include in your list mattered. Who you chose to put first mattered. And who you chose to exclude from the list mattered more than anything.

**Did you remove me
from your MySpace
top 8!!? What did I do?**

Choosing to remove someone who you'd had a falling out with, or who you wanted to have a falling out with, sent a clear message. But the quizzes, notes, and the never-ending dilemma of changing your profile song, couldn't compete with the introduction of Facebook, just as we were all leaving school.

Facebook felt like the perfect combination of the best elements of MSN Messenger and MySpace. Now we could upload photos and send messages to each other quickly and easily. We could also post riveting and essential status updates to our friends, keeping them up to date with our successes and dramas.

We'd go on nights out, take hundreds of grainy photos on our state-of-the-art 8MP digital cameras, and immediately upload them to Facebook. We were sweaty and make-up free because we didn't know how to properly apply it and we were delighted by the fact that we could go out until 3am and buy a pitcher of vodka and coke for only a fiver. We danced on sticky floors, requesting our favourite songs, and we'd hold hands on the walk to the chippy on the way home, talking loudly about our futures.

Then people started to head to uni or away on their gap years. Some friends dropped away, just like Sally had. New photos were uploaded with new friends in exciting new locations.

And the years ticked by, unfolding as a slider of dates at the bottom of our profiles. 2007, 2008, 2009, 2010, 2011. We were posting statuses less and less often, using the new Facebook Messenger more. We were more selective with photographs and set up filters so we could approve posts before they would appear on our walls. We started to trickle out of university and into the world of work where we were warned that our online selves could cost us our careers and so we tightened up our privacy and created names that were ours but not really.

Sa Rah has a birthday today. Wish her the best!

We didn't have to remember birthdays because Facebook would remind us. I knew Leah's was September but I just forgot the exact date. If someone lost their mobile, whole groups were created to harvest all of those lost contacts. Events were organised online and invites sent to profiles. If someone had never joined or decided to leave the platform, sometimes they weren't told. *It's just so convenient and easy, why are some people so difficult?*

Are you sure you want to deactivate your account? Your friends will miss you!

I left Facebook in 2016. As my friends and I started to become busier, building our lives, our families, our careers, I noticed that some other friends started slipping away. There's no better way to describe it because it was so gradual it almost went unnoticed.

Sometimes I forget the exact date of birthdays but I'm trying to be better. I've been forgotten about for events but most friends make the effort to text me. Mostly I don't feel like I'm missing anything at all because my friends have changed the way they're using social networks too.

Becky
Guys can I ask you something?

Megan
Always. I'm in a terrible meeting.

Becky
Have you ever had a 10 day period!??

My main group of friends are a mix of the very oldest (girls I've known since nursery) and the relatively new (friendships forged during high school). Some of them live nearby and others live further away and the times we see each other in person are, these days, few and far between. So we chat as a group via WhatsApp, sometimes frequently and sometimes less often. You can wake up to 100 messages about a single internet video. We can share our innermost fears and worries without judgement and know we have a group of cheerleaders if we have a job interview or an appraisal or a date. We've commiserated and grown angry when one of us has been ghosted and shared excitement when dates turn into something more.

Megan
Yes! I honestly had a period for about 2 weeks once.

Laura
I haven't but I'm pretty sure that's fairly normal.

Becky
Urgh thank god. Was getting worried. Honestly just blood
EVERYWHERE.

My phone buzzes and I lift it from the table to read an ongoing conversation about periods. *How long is too long? How much does it hurt for you? Is this normal? Is that?* All these questions and subtexts come flying through cyberspace to pop up on my screen in the steamy café I'm sat in, clothes damp from a heavy July rain. The answers come just as quickly: *I've had that, it's like that for me too, it's normal, you're normal.*

Beneath the relief of knowing that your body has not betrayed you is something deeper and even more reassuring: that a space exists to ask these kinds of questions and there are people there to support you. Our connected lives can at times feel like a curse but I like to think about these networks of sisterhood operating across the globe like a secret resistance movement.

My relationship with technology has shifted and grown as I have grown myself. From broadcasting all my feelings and insecurities to subtweeting and stalking, I've reached a point where I feel a sense of equilibrium. I now use it to supplement those relationships I hold dearest, to keep in touch when we're far apart. They aren't the same as a face-to-face interaction but that doesn't stop them from being meaningful moments.

I love to receive voice notes from my friends and photos of their date-night outfits. I like hearing about their frustrations at work and their interviews and engagements. I like all of this because they're reaching out to me and because these messages are private. I still like to see holiday snaps on Instagram but it doesn't have the same feeling as someone reaching out and saying, 'I did this and I want you to know because I care about you and miss you'.

So despite all its flaws, I'm grateful that technology has given me this space. I love the idea that around the world, every minute, similar conversations are occurring; women are sharing what's on their mind with their friends, no matter where they are. This is communication without borders, delivery times and time-zone constraints; this is our digital sisterhood.

AN OPEN LETTER TO A FRIEND FORGOTTEN

JADE GREENE

I'm sitting in a hospital in what can only be described as a holding pen. It's small with too many chairs, the walls a light cream or pink, the fluorescent light too bright. There's a box of tissues on a small coffee table in the corner and the wall is adorned with a single picture of a plant, or something equally inoffensive, in a cheap wooden frame. Beneath it is a hole in the wall. This is the Bad News Room and I have a choice to make: surgery, medical management or natural. For the first time in years, I think of you.

I couldn't understand you at first, with your *t'ick oirish accent*. I was always proud of being 'a little bit Irish' (which meant I visited twice in my teens and met distant relatives who I never spoke to again), but you were fresh from the Emerald Isle, plonked in the middle of the Big Smoke. You seemed fierce, impenetrable. But you weren't.

We worked in a too-busy bar, dancing to forbidden 80s pop as we poured, beckoning dithering punters through the crowd with tongue-in-cheek shouts of, 'I'll take you up my end, sir!' We bonded over cheap wine and countless nights in a tiny pub that spilled out into the alleyway, leaning on ledges, feet straddling piss and spilt beer that trickled down from the bins. You can't hide class.

The almost nightly, 'Just for one,' meant a bottle, and a bottle meant two, the closing bell ringing with, 'Onto the next!' as we tumbled down into a dingy speakeasy, leaving London at the door.

It was here, in these toilets, where I held your hand and rubbed your back, your tears pooling and smudging mascara onto my chest. My back hurt leaning over you like that, but you wrenched me closer, heaving with the contraction that coursed through you, your body shaking and sweating, the pain palpable.

I coached you through deep breathing, whispering, 'It will be okay, it will be okay.' What did I know? Feigning the calm midwife, just like the movies. But this wasn't labour. This was miscarriage.

This was how you learnt you were pregnant.

One in four, we read at the pub the following night. This happens to one in four. Four girls around a wonky table. Four glasses of wine left untouched. Four pregnancy tests bought the next day. Only yours came back positive. Still positive. We scooped you up in our arms, but shared a glance; a silent, selfish sigh of relief. Not me.

You wanted to go out drinking and who could blame you? So we slapped on mascara and stumbled into the night, drowning in rosé. We danced and laughed and sang to cheesy hits, and I held you tight as the cramps returned and you bled and wept and convulsed night after night, week after week. Once was torture enough, but this ongoing slaughter was inhumane. This wasn't like the movies or television soaps at all. Crumpled over public toilets, begging for your baby.

You had been to the doctor but apparently there was nothing

they could do. I don't know now whether this was true, but I know you shouldn't have gone alone. I know you should have gone back.

But this was bigger than anything I'd experienced before in my meagre twenty-one years. And quieter, too. Nobody outside of our circle knew. The moment your world imploded was reduced to drunken whispers, silent tears and secret runs to toilet cubicles.

The trauma and complexities of grief ate you up – how do you navigate the loss of something you never even knew you had? You developed a tremor, a shake that started in your hand and, spreading like wildfire, built and built into the eruption of a seizure. Peace finally settled in the moments of unconsciousness that followed as I held your hand and stroked your sweat-speckled hair, reminding you where you were as you awoke.

You eventually told your family everything that had happened and they came over to look after you. The bleeding subsided, the seizures settled. Our job contract came to an end and our friendship ebbed away.

'I'm going for a cigarette.' My head snaps up and I'm back in the holding pen. He stands rooted to the ground a moment before opening the door and leaving. I stare at the hole in the wall – a punch mark, surely.

We heard the heartbeat just a week ago. I had stolen a glance back at the ladies sat nervously in the waiting room, a tip of my invisible hat at their invisible strength. An acceptance that I could not be as strong as them. A gratitude that I would not have to.

But now I am one of those ladies. The dimmed lights and the hum of the machine, the cold between my legs and the hard stare at the ceiling. The silence. The, 'I'm sorry'.

I am one in four. I am you.

Only, for me there is something the doctors can do. For me,

there is choice: surgery, medical management or natural. How to pass the products of conception. How to get rid of our dead baby. But rather than grief (that comes later), I am struck by guilt, because I know exactly what choice to make. Because you led me right to it.

And you stay with me, the memory of you, as I'm enveloped by the kindness of the nurses in the hospital. As the delicious cocktail of morphine and anaesthetic travels up my arm and smudges my brain into a luscious cloud. As I awake with the euphoric, drunken joy of, 'it's over'.

I suppose what I'm trying to say is, I'm sorry.

I'm sorry that my trauma washed gently over me with anaesthesia, whilst yours engulfed you like fire.

I'm sorry that, although I held your hand through the flames, I never stayed to soothe your wounds.

And I'm sorry that I never told you I was sorry for your broken heart, for your suffering, for the loss of your baby.

'They may not be in our arms, but they stay forever in our hearts.'

I suppose it's the same with friendship, too.

'*I used to know her...*'

GROWING APART

SEATING ARRANGEMENTS

SARA SHERWOOD

'I've put Isobel next to Jules. They both work for charities; they'll have loads to talk about. I've sat vegan Thom next to Nisha; she works for The Co-Op. I think that works, right? They'll probably talk about…the co-operative movement?'

'Chartism? The Peterloo Massacre? Mike Leigh's film? Maxine Peake?'

'No, something more modern.'

'The formation of the welfare state? The miners' strike? The downfall of Thatcher?'

'You're right. Thatcher. That'll get their knickers wet.'

'Hate can be a powerful aphrodisiac. Hating the same people is how we became friends.'

'I suppose. He works in sustainability, so they can talk about… plastics? *Blue Planet*? Do you understand what he actually does? I'm too embarrassed to ask again.'

'No. He uses so much jargon that I just stop listening when he talks.'

'He does tend to drone. And your incredible skills at withstanding droning in mind, I've put you next to Thom. I'm on your other side and Jack is next to me.'

'Sounds good,' I say. Poppy has used her calligraphy pens to create individual place-cards for all the guests. I run my finger over the loops of your name. 'Why don't you swap me and Isobel? You're the only one who likes her.' I reach my hand towards Isobel's name card.

'No movement!' She adjusts the place card even though I didn't touch it. 'And I'm not subjecting you to that. You've met Jules, haven't you? The one who came to the pub with Jack the other night and bored on about Paul Thomas Anderson films. I was like, yes, Jules, I too have seen *The Grand Budapest Hotel*.'

I could just tell Poppy. Tell her that my pillow still smells of you. That my tongue was in your cunt less than six hours ago. That when you made me cum with your fingers this afternoon, I bit your shoulder and my teeth marks were dented against your skin. That three weeks ago, when you were curled against my back, your snores fluttering against my neck, I told you that I loved you.

'That's Wes Anderson. And yes, I have met Jules before.'

'Whatever. Still a man with a camera.'

'Have you ever noticed how Isobel says her parents worked really hard to send her to private school? And she once said she *really admired* Michael Gove?'

'Let's not get into that again. What do you think of the table? Nice, right?'

'Yeah. You've got chairs. And plates, I'm assuming.'

'Yes, and cutlery.' Poppy turns to me. She takes a deep breath.

'Do you think people will think I'm a twat because I've bought a house and I'm showing off with a dinner party?'

I shuffle my arm around Poppy's shoulder.

'People won't think you're a twat unless you ask them to bring their own wine.'

Poppy is silent.

'You didn't ask people to bring their own wine, did you?'

Poppy remains silent. I withdraw my arm.

'You could afford a *house*, but you couldn't buy a couple bottles of wine?'

'Half a house. Half a deposit for a house.'

'You're right. Famously, houses, compared to wine, are cheap.'

'There was so much to carry from Tesco, I couldn't add wine!'

'Should have thought ahead and bought a car instead of a house.'

'Meg.'

'Nobody will think you're a twat,' I say. 'They're coming because they love you. And want to believe the rumours are true and new-build houses don't have suspicious patches of damp.'

The doorbell rings. It's not the head-splitting buzz that Poppy and I had in our old flat. I wonder if it's you. My stomach dances at the thought.

'That'll be Isobel,' Poppy says, turning towards the hallway. 'I told her to come early so I could give her a tour of the house.'

'She *asked* for a tour of the house, didn't she?'

'Yes.'

'Hang on,' I say, looking back around the table. 'I'm the only one you haven't paired up.'

'You're with me. We haven't done something together for ages.'

'I wouldn't really call this doing something together.'

'I know. It's just been mental. I *still* haven't found a new assistant at work and buying a house is…exhausting.'

Exhausting, sure. But Poppy still had time to go to a sixtieth birthday party for Jack's aunt last weekend. I saw on her Instagram. I didn't double tap to like it. I screenshotted it and sent it to you.

'What about your boyfriend? You know, Jack? The one you've just committed to a twenty-five-year loan with?'

'Yeah, but he's not you.'

You're the last to arrive.

'Is that Jules?' Isobel whispers to me when you walk into the living room, kiss Poppy on the cheek, and push a pack of Peroni onto the kitchen counter. Isobel giggles behind her glass of Prosecco.

'That is Jules,' I affirm. I could tell her that your cheeks are as smooth as a fresh peach. That one of my favourite things to do is run the tip of my nose along your cheekbone while we're watching *Coronation Street*.

'I'm really into that whole *look* now. My last girlfriend was much more like me. Like femme, you know? I think it's something to do with getting older.'

'I've started to like mackerel as I've gotten older.'

Isobel gives me a withering look. I recognise it from Nicky Robinson's reign of terror in high school. It makes me want to lock myself in the toilets and put my feet up on the door, so nobody knows I'm there. Nicky Robinson's withering looks only stopped in year ten, because Poppy told her to stop calling me a dyke or she would show everyone the picture she'd taken of Nicky giving Harry Riley a blow job on the coach back from Beamish.

'Have you met her before?' Isobel asks, nodding discreetly towards you.

I met you at Poppy's twenty-ninth birthday. Before we were introduced, Poppy whispered that you're the only girl on Jack's five-a-side football team. That was six months ago. Your hair was darker then; it gets lighter in the summer.

'Poppy said she's really smart.'

'She is.'

Throughout the pear-and-fennel-salad starter, Isobel keeps circling a finger around the rim of her wine glass, nodding sympathetically at your transport woes. You haven't had an on-time train for five months.

'The other day, I needed to get from Leeds to Huddersfield and it was delayed by forty-five minutes. Then it was cancelled. I could have got the bus. This was at 8.30am so there was just me and this platform of mardy men huffing about renationalisation.'

I know all this. You keep a spreadsheet of your delayed trains. I don't know what you're going to do with it. Maybe it's just proof that your annoyance exists, that we exist, that you get a train from my flat in Leeds to Huddersfield in the morning.

'Why were you in Leeds?' Jack asks.

'Just a meeting.'

'At 8.30am?'

'It was a breakfast meeting.'

'Those corporate donors must be riding you pretty hard if you're finishing a meeting for 8.30am.'

'Thom,' I say, 'what are the top three things you miss about dairy?'

He gives me a patronising smile. 'Nothing, actually.'

'Not even pizza? I think I'd miss pizza the most. Pizza and yoghurt. Don't you miss yoghurt? Do you have soya yoghurt instead?'

'First off, soya is unethical. And unsustainable.'

'Unsustainable?' Poppy says, pinching my thigh under the table. 'How so?'

'So, come on, Jack,' Nisha calls down the table after he and Poppy have served the poached-rhubarb dessert and put our plates in the dishwasher, 'how much was the deposit?'

Poppy shakes her head. Talking about the pile of money that was waiting for her when her estranged father died makes Poppy feel grubby.

'Twenty-five grand,' Jack says. 'We got the price down from two-sixty. Nightmare. Wasn't it, Poppy?'

'You can get a place in Wakefield for *half* that.'

'Prices are insane around here. I'm shocked you even managed to get a place.'

'And as soon as anything with a garden and a parking space comes on the market it's gone in *seconds*.'

'We must have looked at about twenty houses. These weird open houses with couples who looked exactly like us. Proper strange, wasn't it, Poppy?'

'Uncanny.'

'That's because you're conforming,' I say. I nudge Poppy's knee with mine, so she knows I'm joking. I'm sort-of joking.

Jack ignores me. 'It's like being stalked by yourself. We went out for a drink with one of the couples. Dead nice. He works in sustainability too, Thom. They've not managed to complete yet though. We're meeting them next week for dinner.'

I think what profoundly irritates me about Jack is his complete confidence that he's leading his life the right way because he sees other people, who look like him, doing exactly the same thing.

'What's your interest rate?'

'Did you have a Help-To-Buy ISA, or a normal one?'

'And, be honest, Jack, did you have help from your parents like Poppy did?'

'We'll all be dead from the climate emergency in ten years anyway, so what does it really matter?' I say. Poppy finds my hand under the table and squeezes it in thanks. Isobel smirks at you. I want to smash my plate over your head when you smile back.

I escape to Poppy's second bedroom which she has forbidden the guests to go in. The rest of the house is well-ordered, but this room is filled with unpacked boxes of Poppy's books and winter coats, and the bike Jack never rides leaning against the wall. I don't want to go back downstairs. Jack is pounding on his guitar and the rest of the guests are singing along to 'Wonderwall'.

'Are you starting a splinter group dinner party?' you ask from the doorway.

'Yes,' I say. 'I'm the Chuka Umunna of dinner parties.'

You laugh. A proper laugh. The same way you laugh when your shirt sleeves are rolled up, you're chopping vegetables, and I tell you about Wendy in HR's thoughts on Tinder. I want you to close the door, put your hands on my wrists, and your mouth on my neck.

You look out onto the landing. There is nobody there, and I can't hear anyone coming up the stairs. You shut the door. 'When do you want to go?'

'Now,' I say, pressing the heels of my hands into my eyes. 'I don't know how much mortgage chat I can take.'

You look at your phone. 'Fuck me, twenty minutes for an Uber.'

'It's the suburbs. I'm surprised they even have Wi-Fi here.' I can hear you tapping at your phone. I pull my hands away from my eyes. 'Were you flirting with Isobel?'

'Isobel's a Tory, of course I wasn't flirting with her.'

'You were very chatty.'

'What would you prefer me to do? Never speak to anyone until you want to tell Poppy we're together?'

'So you were flirting?'

'This is silly.' You look up from your phone. 'We hold hands. You've met my parents. We're together. The only person who doesn't know is Poppy.'

'I'm not telling her yet.'

You look pained. You put your phone back in your pocket. You hesitate. I know what you're going to ask.

'Are you in love with her?'

'What?'

'I know I shouldn't think that. I know that queer women can be friends with straight women without any sexual feelings coming into it. But…come on.'

There was one time that confused me for a while. We were twenty-four, it was a Saturday night and we had spent the day hunting through charity shops in Skipton. Poppy bought a Charles and Diana memorial mug and I bought a slouchy lambswool cardigan that smelled of books. After we had our traditional Saturday night pizza and two bottles of red wine, we were propped up on pillows on Poppy's bed. We were watching an episode of *Gossip Girl* and Poppy's laptop was burning into my thighs. I could hear Poppy's slow breathing and I knew she was about to fall asleep. At that moment, I felt so happy, so complete, and I thought: *I will never meet anyone I love as much as you.*

'Of course I'm not in love with her. She's my best friend. She's disgusting. She does horrible smelling shits with the bathroom door open when she's hungover. I've watched her eat chips off the pavement for a bet.'

'You've told me that story before,' you say.

I lay back. In our old flat, Poppy had stuck glow-in-the-dark stars on the ceiling above her bed. We used to lay on it pretending to know about astrology. She would invent our future lives: my favourite was the one where we ran away to an old farmhouse in the Highlands. We would knit our own clothes, tend the vegetable garden and the chickens, and write our novels.

'If I tell Poppy then we'll become Jules-and-Meg who hang out with Poppy-and-Jack. We'll just be another one of their couple friends put on dinner party rotation.'

'She wouldn't do that to you.' You sit down next to me and run your hand over my thigh. 'I just think you should be honest with her.'

But I don't want to be honest with her. When Poppy left our flat, our damp, magical flat in Headingley, to move in with Jack, she gave all the secret parts of herself, which had been for me and her, to him. And now I want to keep something of me from her. To spite her. To punish her for treating our friendship, our home and our life together, as a prelude to something more meaningful with Jack. She has never been my second-best. But she made me hers.

'She'd want to know how happy you are. You are happy, aren't you?'

I sit up and kiss you. I run my hand over the bristles of your undercut. I love the feel of it under my fingers. I pull away and put my forehead to yours.

'Of course I'm happy.'

Voices are on the landing: Nisha and Poppy. You stand up. The door opens.

'I've been looking for you!' Poppy cries. The glass in her hand sways and white wine sloshes onto the carpet. 'Isobel just cornered me to tell me how much mon—'

Poppy stops when she sees you.

'Hi Jules,' Poppy says. Normally, she's too polite to look confused, but the white wine amplifies her voice and exaggerates her expressions. She is creeping towards the dramatic, flouncing Poppy who used to drink cider and chain-smoke outside pubs. 'What are you doing here?'

'I was looking for the bathroom.'

'There's one downstairs, next to the front door. Nisha's in the upstairs one.'

You slide past her and close the door behind you. I hear you clatter down the stairs. Poppy hides her laugh behind her hands.

'I think she fancies you.'

'Best break it to Isobel. I hope she hasn't picked out her wedding power suit.'

'Honestly, Jules was staring at you all the way through dinner.'

'Maybe there was something in my teeth.'

'Why are you even up here?' Poppy asks. She sits down on the bed next to me. 'Tweeting about how much you hate this house party?'

'Headache,' I say. 'Oasis.'

'He doesn't know any Carly Rae Jepsen, sorry.'

'I don't understand how you can love someone who plays a guitar at house parties.'

'Well, firstly, it's a dinner party.'

'You're right. Guitars are more acceptable if there's a sit-down element to the evening.'

'Come back downstairs.' Poppy nudges me. 'I'll have a secret cigarette with you in the garden.'

It's cruel that Poppy treats our old habits as nostalgia. She used to fool me into thinking I had her back: the Poppy that drank a bottle of white wine on a Tuesday night, the Poppy who sent me urgent pictures from the Zara dressing room to help her decide what to buy, the Poppy who would buy two Diet Cokes and two Kinder Buenos on her way home from work. But she always returns to her new life with Jack, leaving me Poppy-less again.

'Given up.'

'Pussy. Since when?'

'Couple of months ago.'

Someone is coming upstairs. I know it's you from the way you jump the last step and give the door two sturdy knocks. You have your denim jacket on, your backpack on your shoulders.

'Poppy, thanks for having me over. Dinner was great.' You lean down and kiss Poppy on the cheek. 'I've gotta dash; got an early start tomorrow. Megan, do you want to jump in the Uber with me? I'll be going past Dock Street, so…'

'You can stay here if you want,' Poppy says to me.

'That's OK. I'll come with you, Jules.'

'No, stay! We've already been calling this Meg's room,' Poppy nudges my shoulder. 'You can pick whatever colour you want for the walls.'

'Megan's got her own room in her own flat,' you say. There's a hint of impatience in your voice.

Poppy turns to you, running her tongue along her teeth, ready to take a bite.

'How do you know where Meg lives, Jules?'

You hesitate. I hesitate.

'I've been to Megan's flat before.'

'Have you?' Poppy says. There's schoolgirl mocking in her voice.

I know you can hear it. I feel anger alight in my blood 'Why?'

'We're seeing each other,' I say, lightly. Poppy turns to me. The laughter falls out of her smile.

Your phone vibrates in your jeans pocket. 'The Uber is here. I'll wait for you downstairs, Megan.'

I get off the bed. Poppy stays where she is.

'Are you joking?'

'No.'

'Seeing Jules?'

'Yes.'

'Jack's Jules?'

My Jules.

'Poppy, I have to go. My taxi's here. We can talk about it tomorrow.'

'You can't just leave after telling me that. How long have you been seeing each other?'

'A couple of months.'

'Months? What the fuck, Meg. Why didn't you tell me?'

I have never wanted to hurt her before. But when her name falls into the graveyard of my WhatsApp, when she keeps missing the beat in our private jokes, when our trips to the pub, the cinema, to bottomless brunch always include Jack, when she talks about the holidays I'm not on, when she talks about the future that castrates me into her fucking guest bedroom, she is kindling a universe of hurt.

'Because I didn't want to.'

We pull away from Poppy's new house. You are looking out of the window. Poppy is standing on her front step, looking at me, neither smiling nor waving. I know she's going to cry; her wobbling chin always betrays her.

'You were right to tell her,' you say. 'She'll get over it.'

'I know.' I'm watching Poppy. She doesn't look away as we leave.

I know that when we're out of sight, Poppy will walk upstairs, lock herself in the bathroom and cry into a towel. I used to be the one who sat outside the door, asking her if she was OK, if she wanted to talk about it. She would never answer, but I would always make her a cup of tea – milky with a heap of sugar – and leave it outside the door. I hope Jack knows to leave it there, and that she doesn't mind if it goes cold before she unlocks the door.

MEMORIES OF HONEY

ALICE GODLIMAN

'You have memories to look back on today'

I.

Our knees touch as we sunbathe
Legs dusty against the warm pavement
Street sticky with syrupy heat.
Three cigarette ends sit abandoned, lonely
Next to my pale calf.
Seeming anaemic against her golden colour and warmth
Her sun casting a cocoa-butter sheen over the quiet street and
    lonely shops.
The moon next to her looks pale and uninteresting,
    almost invisible.

She always coats my memories with spiky sweetness
Like honeycomb,
Like the Diet Coke we chug obsessively,
Swapping barbs of observation or a shared annotation.
Once she wrote
'Aeneas is a dick'
In the margin of his myth and I wrote it too.

2.

      We shrieked;
      We squealed;
      We screamed.
The soundtrack buzzing at an octave too high.
We deserved the glares and flinches and eyerolls,
But they didn't understand:
Everything is so exciting when you find your soulmate
Your soul's sister
Your other half.
The end to your unfinished sentences
The start to your sentence ends.

3.

We shared our cigarettes and traumas
Counted calories and hours studying.
You told me about purging after dinner
And I told you about the sharp blade in my purse.
We cried.
You told me you're forgetful when you're hungry.
And I am too.
We held hands and shared honey and chocolate ice cream.

4.

We planned our futures
Our children will be best friends
You'll have a personal assistant called Tarquin
I'll be a starving writer and you'll be paying my bills
I'll have a cat called Clytemnestra
And you'll have dogs.

5.

Three years since the last time we met on purpose
And we're both bra shopping in M&S
Incidental.
The hug feels natural
But the silent air is thick like syrup
And we're an octave lower than we used to be
As if we need sweet lemon tea to soothe a throat unused
    to talking.

You've moved in with your boyfriend.
And I remember the times we laughed about him
In the 'friendzone' you said, his romantic feelings unrequited.
Not anymore.

But I miss the friendzone
Have been out of it for longer than he was in it.

We say we'll get drinks.

6.

Once your name had been sweet like sunlight in my mouth,
Cloying like honey.
Always there at the tip of my tongue, star of my anecdotes.
My mother tired of hearing your opinions in my voice.
Those times when I wanted to talk but had nothing to say
You were what I talked of.
The aftertaste of those times remain
Sometimes your name surfaces with no story to attach to it.

7.

'You have memories to look back on today'
Every day your name stings me.
Often attached to some all-caps musings.
Photos. Our feet, two pairs of opaque tights and high heels
And sat on a sofa with popcorn and *Hercules*
And watching TV on your phone in the common room
And drinks and haircuts and push up bras and wide eyed
   gesticulating and shared clothes and costume parties and
   bottles of Lambrini and my lipstick on your cheek and posing
   next to our favourite teacher and my first Pride and prom
   dresses and short shorts and pyjamas and—

8.

Once your mum made rum punch and
Later
I kissed your new best friend
You told me I needed to pick a side.
You were wrong, but also right.

9.

I have memories to look back on, or forward to today.
I could tell you about them.

> I 'picked a side', my mum got sick, my mum got better.
> I don't drink anymore, I quit my job, I'm moving house.
> I still count calories, but not very well, and you'll never
> > guess what happened yesterday.

All those things I want to say.
But I can't finish your sentences anymore, and you can't
> start mine.
I have memories of honey, but also the bee's sting when it isn't
> the same.
So I could call you,
But I shouldn't.

FIRECRACKER

HUMA QURESHI

It's the night before my wedding and you lie barefoot on my hotel bed lounging back on the pillows as if you own the place. Remote control in one hand, your shoes strewn across the floor, crumpled clothes discarded in a trailing heap. I shake them out, fold them up, place them in a neat pile upon the sideboard.

You could at least….! I say and you laugh, make some joke about how you hope marriage might lighten up my austere, tidy ways. I laugh too but honestly I am not joking for I have always hated this habit of yours, the messy carelessness which means I am forever picking up after you while you are forever losing things. Pieces of jewellery, library books, your mobile phone.

Eventually this will happen to us: you will drop bits of our friendship here and there and eventually, I will stop picking us back up, picking you back up, putting us back together again. Eventually we might forget where we put it, this friendship of ours, and we will both let it fall through the cracks of a floorboard, forgotten in the memory of old mix tapes and letters boxed in an attic somewhere.

But tonight you fall asleep on my bed. I nudge you with my foot, shake your shoulder. We have shared many milestones but I want to be on my own tonight. *Alright, alright!* and you smile your fabulous crooked smile and slope out of my room into yours next door.

The next morning, you are late to my wedding. I don't even know when you arrive.

Later I will wonder if this was the moment things changed. The moment you practically missed my wedding because you were drunk, passed out in your room. The moment I kicked you out of my room into your own. The moment you started losing me, we started losing each other. But then I realise: it had already happened long, long before.

We meet at university. We are eighteen. The way you tell the story, you say you stood in my doorway and talked and talked and talked so much that I begrudgingly invited you into my room just to shut you up. You tell people we stayed up talking so late, you fell asleep on my floor. This part is untrue but I stopped correcting you a long time ago.

Truth is, you always stay too long. *I am literally throwing you out right now!* I yell and you cackle and duck as I throw your scarf or your jumper at your head. In this way you are like the sibling I have never had, annoying but beloved in equal measure.

At university I routinely pick up all the things you scatter in my room over the course of an average day – a cardigan, a hair-band, eyeliner, lip balm, a bunch of old magazines – and place them outside your door when you are asleep. Sometimes you mess up my bookshelves or my desk on purpose. *Would you look at that,* you say. *Oops.*

Despite your attitude to orderliness, I am drawn to you by the way you talk endlessly and the things you say and this is how we become friends in the first place. You talk like poetry. You fizz like lemonade, bittersweet; you do not care what other people think of your clothes or the wild way you dance. You are dreamlike with the sort of face that does not even need make-up. Many boys fall in love with you and later so too will many men but you pretend not to care. One night you decide to kiss as many boys as you can; it is a game to you. You are writing a book already and you have this air of knowing artfulness and because I trust you, I show you the short stories I have written that I have never shown anyone else (even though you never show me anything you have written yourself).

It does not take me long to understand that your stream of talking is some kind of front because there are other edges to you, frail edges. Sometimes you cloud over. You disappear. You fade out as though I've lost you for a minute or two to some other frequency, some other conversation in your head. *Hey,* I say, *Where'd you go?* And you blink, shake your head and smile and that's always the end of it.

You let things slip about your parents, how you feel like an awkward piece of inherited furniture they are obliged to hold onto. You were in trouble at school and because of this your father gives up on you and calls you chaotic, misspent. You tell me you feel rootless and in times like these, when your sad thoughts empty out like lonely pennies, I squeeze your hand because I know you do not share this with anyone else, but then you disappear, a will-o'-the-wisp, into that other place in your head again.

You are witty, clever, but you skip lectures all the time and you are not the least bit concerned. All you read are back copies of *Vogue*.

You say you don't care about studying because of the book you are writing, which someone in publishing had told you showed great promise. The entirety of university is like a gap year to you, an escape from your parents to do whatever you want to do and boy, you do everything you can get your hands on. But me, I fret a lot over my grades, over my future, about being sensible and making the right choices. Times like these you pull me up onto my feet to dance. *You take things too seriously,* you tell me, head thrown back, drink in hand. *But Lou,* I want to say. *You don't take things seriously enough.*

You stay with me over the long summer holidays. Because you talk so damn much you charm my parents with your chattiness and your beauty, your livewire energy. *Firecracker*, my mother calls you. One night you tell me you love my life and I burst out laughing because I know you cannot mean it; I am ordinary and grew up in the suburbs but you grew up in London and everything about you is bespoke. *But I do*, you say. *I mean it entirely.*

We graduate. I try not to make a big deal of it because you did not do as well as the rest of us and even though you say you do not care, I know you do.

The rest of us are making plans for our futures. I line up unpaid internships on magazines because eventually I want to be the sort of writer who might even get paid, and because we both want to write for a living I offer to share the contacts I make. But you tell me you have other plans, plans for the book you've been writing ever since before we started university. Your cheeks burn, your skin glows, and you say you still can't tell me more about it yet, but that it's going to happen for you, your book, your name in print. *I believe you*, I tell you, *I believe in you*, even though you've never shown me a word you've written before.

You insist I stay with you in your parents' flat in west London while I'm interning and you squeal like a small child at the prospect of us playing house. Your parents are away and so at first my stay feels hilarious, a carefree holiday, but my days interning are long and uninspiring. In the frustration of working for free, I spend my evenings searching online for paid work. I stay up late applying for junior roles on newspapers, writing cover letters, drafting emails to editors. You leave me be initially (besides you tell me you are writing your book) but soon you begin to constantly interrupt. *Come out for ice cream! Let's get pizza!* you say. Or *Dance! I want to dance!* You do not knock, you never knock, and when you say these things it is always late at night when I am in my pyjamas and you are in some wacky outfit, your eyes burning bright as though you are on fire. *I am trying to find work*, I say. *Lou, I have stuff to do.* Times like this you make me mad. In my head, I want to say *What's wrong with you? How old are you, like five?* But finally you give up. You shut my door without a wisecrack and you leave without messing anything up.

We begin to see less of each other even though we live in the same place. Sometimes you are gone for days. There are times I don't hear from you and then when I do, your messages make little sense, odd manic messages which I think are made up but I cannot be sure. *I am in Paris! Looking for a cat! I have gone to Camden to buy a hat! I am working on my prologue from a man's bed!*

You lose your keys at least three times a week. Sometimes you blow hot and cold like a monsoon storm. I overhear you arguing with your parents on the phone and though your face is shadowed and stained afterwards and though I try to tell you I'm here for you, you pretend like it never happened at all. One night I find you curled up, bruised and crying on the floor and yet still you do not tell me what's wrong.

At university you were always what our other friends called random because you did things like quote Shakespeare to strangers and wear daisy garlands and summer dresses in the thick of winter and because you also did that thing whereby you went somewhere else in your head, but I always stood up for you. *She's not strange*, I would say. *She's poetic. Creative. Give her a break.*

I always loved your ability to see wit and beauty in ordinary things. But now your intensity is making my head spin because I do not know what's going on with you, because you will not tell me what it means when you slam the window or the door or lock yourself in the bathroom. You do not like meeting up with our other friends anymore and I make excuses for you in front of them. They ask how you are only now I do not know what to say so I sigh, *Hard times.* They ask if you have a job and I shake my head. *To be honest I never really understood how the two of you were such good friends,* one of them says.

Meanwhile your flat is a mess. It is more than a mess. It is dirty. I come back from interning and open the windows, make your bed. At university this too was part of your charm: your unbrushed hair, the romance of an abundance of vintage clothes draped on the back of a chair. But here in the real world, it is petulant, lazy. *Laissez faire,* you say as I vacuum around you. Washing your dishes, doing your laundry. I am grateful for having a place to stay but I am angry with you for living this way.

I ask how your book is going. You tell me it's nearly finished.

I get a job on a newspaper with a decent-enough salary and because I have met someone and because I need normality and space and somewhere clean to live, I want to rent a flat of my own. But I feel guilty for even thinking it, more guilty than you will ever know, as though I am leaving you behind. But I am beginning to hate living with you. It is too much, like overwhelming perfume that turns my stomach and hurts my head. I have to move.

Years later I will see a film about a young woman in north London who died in her flat and wasn't found for three years and for weeks I will have nightmares that the young woman could have been you.

When your parents return I leave, even though I hate myself for doing this to you. I do not know if you ever forgive me for leaving you with them but you watch me pack with a rage burning upon your skin. *Be seeing you, hope not sporadically* you say, a line from some dumb movie we both liked, as you shut the door.

But without the pressure of living just the two of us, the fever of our strange friendship breaks like the relief of rain in high summer. There is a space between us now and at first the space is empty but then it widens into a space in which we are eventually able to come together again.

I write you a letter. I tell you it all felt too much but I also tell you that I miss you, that I trust you, that I care and worry about you because you have distanced yourself from so many of our friends and I do not want you to distance yourself from me. When you receive it, you call me and even though I am at work, I pick up straight away because I hoped you would call, knew you would call. You open with a burst of laughter that sounds like a rainbow and then: *Look at us! We're like an old married couple!* You laugh some more and so I do too and then you sniff and say *Sorry for being A Nightmare.* You say you've been thinking it over and the problem is we don't do *stuff* together anymore and so that's what we begin to do, stuff: dancing, movies, cocktails and, although it takes a few months to find our rhythm, for a while it is as though we are back at university again.

I have my own place now and when you first come to visit you run your finger along the mantlepiece and say *Hmm* like Mary

Poppins which cracks us both up. You often come over and still stay too late. You have lost weight so I feed you carbs, baked potatoes as big as our heads, and you talk and talk and talk and we laugh and laugh and laugh and though I always plan to talk to you about it properly, face-to-face, about those months when I stayed with you and you seemed like you were falling apart, weekends like these reassure me that you are okay, that you are not lost, that you are not lonely or being left behind.

One time when you're raiding my fridge, you tell me how you feel so frozen some days you physically cannot move. You're seeing a therapist now and finding your way through the dark and you just throw this information out there and then you tell me I'm out of milk. You switch the subject back to the boy I'm dating and you tease me about him like a teen, asking ridiculous questions about his kissing technique. I throw a cushion at your head and you stick your tongue out at me on your way to the fold-out sofa bed.

After you leave, I always find something you have left behind. A crumpled train ticket. A bottle of perfume. A hairbrush. It is as though you do it on purpose.

We turn thirty. I have just got engaged.

Do you really love him? you want to know and the way you say it, it's with a hint of distaste. I say I do and then you press me for more, but I keep it to myself because you sleep with men but you do not fall in love with them and I do not want to make you feel judged or alone. You joke about me being married and having babies and moving to the suburbs and I let you make that joke before asking if you'll ever settle down, have a proper relationship now. You almost spit your coffee out with laughter and then you call yourself a spinster, somebody's mistress at best, but there's a sadness behind the way you say it so then I don't ever bring the subject up again.

The first time you meet him, the man who will eventually ask me to be his wife, you turn up in a polka dot dress with a stiff petticoat underneath it, like fancy dress, and you talk licketysplit, a character from a cartoon. Later I ask him what he thinks of you. He smiles and says you're a little crazy, like a whirlwind, which is something people have often said about you. *Wouldn't put the two of you together is all*, he calls from the kitchen. I smile too, because I imagine you must think the same about him and me.

Yet several months later you throw yourself into my wedding with a fervour that surprises me, especially because I do not even ask it of you. I don't even want a hen do but you press one upon me with such unprecedented enthusiasm, giddy and girly, I don't stop you. You gather the friends I love together like flowers, even the ones who used to be your friends too, the ones with whom you had fallen out of touch. When you are with them you act as though you had never deliberately distanced yourself from them at all. You decorate the restaurant with fairy lights and gauzy drapes and it's all so theatrical, all so pretty, and I'm all so touched I cry. *I just want to do this for you*, you whisper in my ear. I feel bad for saying it but honestly, I didn't think you could pull it off.

But despite all this, a couple of weekends later you still pass out drunk in your hotel room the night before my wedding and end up missing most of it and that's when I really begin to wonder what the hell is wrong with you.

After my honeymoon, you turn up on my doorstep with flowers and a basket of biscuits, a tulle ribbon in your hair. It's only flowers and only biscuits and you missed my wedding for God's sake, but I still forgive you. I forgive you because I feel sorry for you. But I also forgive you because I care. You tell me you don't know why you acted the way you did, that things got out of hand, that you drank because you were a little sad and felt frozen again. *The ice is melting now*, you say.

I forgive you because I wish things had turned out differently for you. I wish you had parents who prioritised you and I wish you felt loved and I wish something had become of the book you told us you were writing because honestly, I think that might have saved you most of all. I forgive you because you're still that person who charmed me utterly into being her friend, stood in my doorway, talking and talking and talking of marvellous, unbelievable things.

But then you go dark. Of all the things to do, you go dark. You turn your landline off and your mobile phone off too and I cannot reach you at all. I think about that film I had seen with the young woman with lots of friends but also no friends, lying dead and undiscovered for years and now that so much has passed, I begin to believe that might actually, truly, happen to you too.

Then out of the blue, weeks and weeks later, you come back as though nothing has happened at all. I'm mad at you but you tease me, call me *worrywart* in a singsong voice. You tell me you're researching your book and I know that this is a total lie because every time in the last twelve years that I have asked you about it, you are never able to give anything away.

You turn your phone on, you turn it off. I can't keep track of where you're at.

I have a baby. I think of you from time to time.

I invite you round for lunch because I haven't seen you for over seven months when I told you I was pregnant and I haven't heard from you since my baby was born, apart from a text message of

Congrats! when I sent you a photo the day after he arrived. *Are you sure you want her to come?*, my husband asks and I say *yes*, because I get the feeling that if I don't call you over, I might not ever see you again.

We all have those friends, the ones we can go months without seeing yet it feels like no time at all has passed when they walk in the door. We all have those friends who ground us. But you are not that sort of friend and this feeling of ease, of comfort and long-term connection, does not come into my home with you.

It is a strange lunch, strange in its mundanity. You have a job now, an assistant in some tech start-up, and from this I deduce your book never did come out, if it was even written at all. You talk so politely, it is as though you are holding it in, the sharp smartass comments about my decline into domesticity, a baby attached to my breast, a tidy three-bedroom house. You hold my baby and he tugs your necklace off and you pass him back to me.

I wish I could say there had been some drama, that we had some falling out when we sat down to the table for our lasagne lunch, if only to make sense of how our friendship went from being so all-consuming to merely a memory of my twenties. If only to understand how you went from being someone who always stayed too long, someone I had to literally shove out the door, to being someone I just happened to know some time ago.

I text you to thank you for coming but you never reply. I wonder if perhaps you've lost your phone so later at Christmas I send you a card and then another on your birthday too. In between I email, nothing much simply wondering how you are, but you never write back so I stop. But I am not angry at you. I understand. I accept time has passed and we have changed and there is an emptiness now in which we have nothing left to say because it has all been said already, because there are no words left between us anymore.

When you come over that last time, you leave your necklace behind, still as forgetful as you ever were. It has an initial on it, only the initial is not even for your name. I do not know whose initial it is. It is another one of those inexplicable wildcard things about you. For a while I keep the necklace safe in a small envelope in the back of a drawer with the intention of giving it back to you when I see you again, but then one day when I am tidying up I set it aside to give to charity.

It is only later that I remember how it even came to be there.

THIS SIDE OF THE MERSEY

HANNAH SIMPSON

Between the clamour of red faces in novelty festive jumpers, eager for immediate service at the bar, I don't notice her come in. It isn't until I'm close enough to thrust one arm between two strangers and lay the tips of my fingers possessively on the sticky wood, that I see her through the heads of the revellers around me.

Natasha Dennis. By all accounts my best friend, ever since the day we made it official by carving our initials into a bench further down the prom from here. I still sit there sometimes, taking my lunch from the café out onto the front when the weather allows. These days, I see more of that battered old seat than I do of her.

She stands beside the long table Lauren and Jenna managed to reserve when they first got here. The pair of them simultaneously embrace Tash as she leans down to hug them both in one fell swoop. Her frothy cappuccino hair is tied into a familiar messy bun that sits on the top of her head; it began as a way to stop it from getting even more tangled by the brutal coastal winds, but I'm happy to see she still wears it this way even now that she lives across the water in a city high-rise. The way Lauren and Jenna look at Tash as she slides out of her coat and unravels her scarf, you'd be forgiven for thinking she was a monarch gracing us with her presence. Since she moved to Liverpool, she's been pretty off the radar – too busy with her new job to make the train journey back under the Mersey to see us. It's hard to believe how much time can pass when you're not paying attention.

Tash gestures around to the empty chairs and even from here I can see Jenna's dramatic eye roll. I don't have to hear her to know what she says next. She's already mentioned twice how pissed off she is that no one else has turned up yet.

I know that the customary thing to do would be to try and catch Tash's eye, or maybe text her to ask what she wants to drink. Instead I avert my gaze, focussing on the harassed barman as he contends with the Christmas Eve crowd.

There used to be nine of us, a big close-knit girl gang who stuck together all through high school. Nine's a good number, we said. Big enough to always have someone to talk to, small enough so that no one gets left out. Of course, some bonds were stronger than others, people naturally gravitating into twos and threes, but that didn't come with any drama. The lot of us were tight. We spent our free time hogging the pool tables in the bowling alley, chasing boys around the Cherry Tree shopping centre and walking as far down the coast as our legs would allow on the warmer days – warm*er*, because it never quite seemed to be properly warm. Tash, with the confidence that came from being the eldest of five, was the ringleader. I'd be lying if I told you that I chose to be her sidekick. She picked me. Back in year eight when Nick Allman broke her heart. Back before the bench became our place. Back when Tash wore her hair long. With her Adidas trainers on the wooden plank and her bum on top of the backrest, she thought the wind that blew her curls across her face would stop me from seeing her tears.

'Hey babe, I didn't see you come in.' Even to my own ears, it sounds false. 'Have you been here long?'

Three heads turn to watch me balancing the glasses precariously between my splayed fingers, making me so self-conscious that I nearly drop them. Tash smiles up at me and says that she's only just arrived. I distribute the drinks before sliding into the space opposite her. As soon as I'm seated, I realise that I should have hugged her. I've missed my chance – it would be too much of a palaver now, a bit too awkward to instigate, so instead I smile back.

'Sorry,' I say automatically. 'If I'd known you were here, I would have got you a drink.'

She shakes her head, waving a hand to indicate that it doesn't matter, and grabs her bag from the floor to head up to the bar herself.

Jenna takes a sip from her glass with an audible sigh of contentment. She had told us, while deliberating over the drinks menu, that she couldn't remember the last time she'd got out of the house on her own.

'Can you believe that Charlie's nearly six months?' she'd asked. 'Where does the time go?' She used to be the wild one, always with an older boyfriend who was happy to buy us booze. She's changed now, much calmer and rounder. She spends less time on her hair and make up, and looks nicer for it. She says being a mum has taken over her life, which I suppose is the way it's meant to be.

I glance in the direction of the bar and see a flashing Rudolph jumper ushering Tash forwards. She smiles and slides into the space he's made for her. She'll be at the front in no time. People have always been generous with Tash – I doubt she's ever waited the full length of a queue in her life.

Lauren wonders aloud where the others are with her brow wrinkled in frustration. Ever the organiser, she picks up her phone from the table and reads out the message as she types it into our group chat.

'Hey...guys. Me, Jenna, Becky and Tash...are here. Where are you...all at?'

When she'd suggested it back in October, everyone had seemed keen. A couple of the girls were a maybe, Rachel was planning her trip to Bali and Steph just didn't reply. Lauren would have known before I responded that I was a definite. I have nowhere else to be. I'd been surprised when Tash had said that she'd put it in her calendar and that she couldn't wait. She hadn't replied to the text I'd sent her the week before, but I hadn't taken it personally until then.

Tash returns from the bar with a glass of Baileys in one hand and her phone in the other.

'It makes a change,' she says, nudging Lauren as she sits back beside her. 'It's normally me who's fashionably late.'

The mood palpably lightens. Tash has always been better at reassurance than me. She actually manages to get Lauren to laugh for the first time since I arrived.

'Excuse me, that chair's taken,' Lauren says sharply to a bearded man in a candy cane patterned shirt who begrudgingly sulks away as she turns her attention back to the table with a smile.

'So what's new?' Tash asks. 'I'm completely out of the loop.'

We make sporadic small talk, skipping around subjects with slightly awkward pauses between topics. It picks up when Jenna tells us that she saw one of our old teachers at her mum-and-baby group, and Tash follows up that her manager is a girl who was the year above us in school. We all comment on what a small world it is, and the girls laugh as Tash reminds us that her now-manager used to work on the tills in the big Morrisons. She stops laughing when she sees that I'm not. Lauren gets excited, telling us that she saw some one-hit-wonder from the noughties last time she was in there, which makes sense since he's in this year's panto. She reminisces about the time she got so drunk on a night out in Liverpool that we convinced her to do his song on karaoke.

'It still makes me cringe thinking about it,' she says, covering her face with her hands. We lovingly laugh at her expense, Tash impersonating how out of time and off key she was.

The group chat lights up four phone screens on the table in front of us. Molly's car won't start and that means she can't pick up Beth. Naomi is typing… She won't be able to join us either, she's way behind wrapping presents. The three of them send sad faces and hearts and promises to do something in the New Year. Jenna gives a tut and mutters that she managed to make it and she has a baby.

'I wonder how long they've been planning to bail,' Lauren says, staring at her phone, unable to hide the bitterness in her voice.

I tell her not to worry about it, that we're having a good time without them, aren't we?

'Well, of course,' says Tash. 'The best of us are here.'

This confirmation is enough to satisfy Lauren, who locks her phone and slides it into her bag.

'I guess,' says Jenna, taking another swig of her rosé.

'And what about you, Becky?' Tash asks. 'How's the café?'

She's only asking to be polite – no one really cares about the café. And the café never changes. I tell her as much, with a self-deprecating shrug. I don't tell them that I'm a manager now. It's hardly impressive news to share and I know they'll think that that's me done. I've settled, I've given up. They'll all smile and say how pleased they are for me, but to my ears it'll sound fake and then everything will feel awkward.

I don't actually mind my job all that much. It pays my bills, gets me out of the house, and at least I don't have to wear a uniform or a suit. I'm more than happy to wipe down tables and make chit-chat with the regulars, who come in for their usual fried breakfast, to keep myself distracted. I've learned how to keep my cool during Mr Thompson's rambling anecdotes, which, no matter how they start, always end on how this town has gone downhill since all them foreigners came over here stealing hard-working men's jobs. I manage to nod politely without commenting on the fact that his son hasn't had a job in years, and something tells me that isn't the fault of the family who run the new Polish supermarket next to the bank. My 'excellent customer service skills' are part of what made me management material, apparently. It's also because they knew I wasn't going anywhere, not with Mum the way she is. Even if I could take my life in a different direction, I'm not sure ten years' experience in a little seaside café is going to look that impressive on a CV.

The conversation meanders along until the dregs of the first drinks are sitting in front of us. The suggestion of a second round is hanging in the air until Jenna clicks the button at the side of her phone to light up the screen.

'God, is that the time already?' She seems genuinely shocked to see that it's all of nearly nine o'clock. 'I should probably go and let Mum off the hook.'

She turns to pull her coat from the back of her chair while asking Lauren if she still wants a lift home.

'Yeah, I best get back and make sure my brothers haven't killed each other yet,' she sighs, standing up and reaching for her bag.

We do the customary round of hugs and Merry Christmasses and promises to do this again soon, as we 'always leave it too long'.

And then it's just me and Tash. We settle back down opposite each other at our end of the long table and exchange tight-lipped smiles. I take a sip from my already-empty wine glass and she pulls out her phone, typing rapidly before sliding it back into her pocket. The silence seems heavy without the others to help carry its weight. She looks down at the sticky menu, scanning the familiar drinks on offer and remarks for the second time this evening at how much cheaper it is here than in Liverpool.

'Even though it's a chain, the prices are different everywhere,' I observe and we both nod as though I've said something profound.

When a woman in a sparkly top and Christmas-tree earrings asks if she can take a chair, we let her. She purses her lips in scorn at the two of us having the gall to be hogging a table this large when the place is chocka.

A long moment passes and then Tash catches my eye and says the word I've been wanting to hear all night. A word that makes my heart fizz momentarily like chips hitting hot oil.

'Bench?'

We're still us – or at least we could be.

To the rest of the world, it's just a battered wooden seat looking out at the river. It's easy to ignore everything on this side of the Mersey – the grey sand and green seaweed-covered rocks littered with washed up condoms and bleached crisp packets – and focus on the tall buildings of Liverpool. That view is one of the best things about living here. The Liverbirds just get to look at our nondescript little coastline. We definitely have the better deal.

The bench has many other markings – *Jonno's a wanker, JT hearts LC, Kelsey's a fat slag* – and bears a brass plaque dedicating it to a lady called Hillary who we would never know anything about other than the dates that book-ended her life, but we consider it ours. We'd spend early mornings, hands clutched around hot chocolate in paper cups, shouting over the wind. Long afternoons, slurping brightly coloured Slush Puppies and making the most of the brief British summer time, pale legs stretched out to optimistically seek the sun. Chilly evenings, warming ourselves on portions of chips – we bounced around from place to place, never settling on one establishment, never finding that elusive perfect chip. We sat on this bench and we laughed and cried and talked about everything in the world, as we watched things change around us. The wasteground, where kids used to skateboard and throw stones at passing cars, was paved over and then up went the cinema, the restaurants, the supermarket. The casino was the real jewel in the crown, the first place in New Brighton you could get a half-decent cocktail.

We lurked behind people who dared to take our seat, stared down couples as we both headed for the same spot, and Tash nearly punched a lad who swore at us and called us lezzas when we asked him to move. The years that passed on this bench were scented with vinegar and sea air and the DKNY she got every birthday. That's what our friendship smelled like.

As we got older and spent our weekends at house parties, we would end up on the bench in the early hours of the morning when the fun started to wind down. We'd wander away from the pounding music, the shrieking and the snogging inside the house, and sit on the silent prom, gazing across at the bright lights of the city. It was the safest place I knew: nothing bad could happen if I was with Tash on our bench. Sharing a bottle of supermarket-own-brand vodka, we talked about all the things we were going to do with our lives. It felt like we were on the edge of something really important, on the brink of becoming exciting, becoming adults. In reality, we were just two drunk teenagers and the only thing we were on the edge of was the Wirral Peninsula.

The wind is so cold that it's hard to focus on anything other than the harsh gusts making my eyes water and my ears ring. Sitting side by side on the damp wooden bench, we both stare out at the blackness that separates us from Liverpool twinkling off in the distance. Unseen, the waves sound ferocious, although they are almost drowned out by the wind as it screams and wails around us. The cold slices straight through all our carefully chosen layers as our cheeks burn red from the chill. Tash's hands are on her bare knees, rubbing rhythmically at the exposed skin above her tall suede boots. She must have forgotten just how cold it gets – she says that you're always sheltered in a city, tall buildings take most of the battering.

Over the salt air and the lingering scent of stale alcohol my coat has picked up from the pub, I can just about make out her familiar perfume. She probably doesn't notice it any more. You can't smell your own smell. While my ponytail blusters in the gap between us, Tash's bun stays tight on top of her head. Even in this weather, she still manages to look stylish. Effortless is the word. She always looks effortless, like life just happens to her and she just copes.

I visited her once, in Liverpool. No bench this time, instead a squashy faux-antique pleather armchair in the corner of an independent coffee shop. Vinegar and cold air replaced by coffee beans and burned cheese from the panini grill; seagulls and the metallic ring from the arcades now the hiss of steamed milk and chatter over ambient muzak. I ordered a coffee and looked blankly at the man with the twirly moustache behind the counter when he asked what type.

'A coffee,' I repeated. Back at the café, saying that would be enough. Seeing his blank stare, Tash jumped in, asking for something Italian which turned out to be exactly what I ordered – a coffee. I spotted her widening her eyes apologetically at the moustache and it made my stomach clench. I'd embarrassed her. We sank down into matching armchairs, sipping from what I would have thought were cereal bowls, and not talking. She kept checking her watch like it was a nervous tick, flicking her wrist over and glancing at the moving hands. She didn't seem to take in the time, merely performing the action to have something to do with her eyes rather than having to look at me. Rather than having to acknowledge the distance between us. The time ticked by and we made vague small talk. We touched on her new exciting job, the guy she'd just started seeing, the fact that the casino back home had closed for good and was that the beginning of the end for the attempt to make us a destination again. Mostly we talked about our old crowd. She'd seen Lauren a few times, brunch here, drinks after work there, but my news mainly came from social media. I asked if she'd seen Jenna's twelve-week scan, pulling the image up on my phone.

'Oh my God, no way!' she said, taking the phone from me to see it more clearly. 'I didn't even know she was pregnant.' Her smile didn't quite reach her eyes. 'I'm missing everything over here.'

The conversation became more animated, discussing Naomi's new dog, Beth's unexpected break-up, how much fun Rachel was having backpacking around Australia. My heart, which had been firmly lodged in my throat, floated back into place and dissolved like sugar into a cup of tea. I felt more comfortable than I had since I met her at the busy train station.

'I'm so glad you came,' she said, putting her hand on my arm. 'It's more lonely than you think, living in a city.'

'Still better than being back at home,' I replied. 'It's not like I see much of anyone either.'

'You've got your reasons though, what with your mum and that.'

It made me feel safe, knowing I didn't have to explain myself to her. She'd always understand. Whatever the future brought, we shared a history that nothing could change. The idea that this was all we had left was one that I rejected vehemently, one that I had to keep pushing to the back of my mind.

'Are you seeing anyone?' She turns her head, raising her voice over the rush of the wind.

'You know all the good ones left for uni and never came back,' I reply, before asking her how James is. She smiles slow and dreamy, like people do in music videos, but rarely in real life.

'That's actually what I wanted to talk about.' She widens her eyes and presses her lips together, as though she has something exciting trying to fight its way out. I'm momentarily distracted by how familiar this face still is to me – the face that told me she was finally going to have a sister when we were twelve, that her family were going to Disneyland when we were fifteen, that she got an A in Geography after two years of worrying she'd fail. And here it was again, meaning the same thing it always did after all this time.

'So…James proposed…' She speaks slowly, relishing the words even if their impact is slightly less dramatic since she's shouting to be heard. I break into a wide smile. Because even if I've never met

James and part of me feels a jolt of nausea at the thought of my oldest friend taking a massive step away from me and towards someone I don't know, I can't help myself being totally and completely happy for her. Instinctively I grab her hand, the first time we've touched all night. Her fingers are freezing.

'That's amazing…congratulations!' I don't instil enough emotion into these three words. I hope they come across as genuine, because they are. I look down at her hand, locked in mine, and notice an absence. 'Could he not afford a ring?' I tease.

'Fuck off,' she says, making the insult loving in a way that only Tash could. 'It's being resized. I can show you a picture.' Her free hand seeks out her phone, but she keeps her other hand in mine. She clicks and scrolls for a silent moment before passing me the phone. A photo of a large angular diamond displayed on her outstretched hand fills the screen. I make a noise that suggests I'm impressed, which I am because the rock is massive.

'I actually wanted to ask you a bit of a favour.' She drags the left side of her lower lip under her front teeth, a surefire sign that she's nervous. I look expectantly at her, not wanting to laugh at how dramatically her tone has shifted. She takes her phone back, clicks the screen off and turns her body so that she's facing me.

'So James's sister is going to be the head bridesmaid or whatever it's called but she's like, thirty five with three kids and there's no way she's planning my hen do.' She glances into the Mersey, and then looks back to me. 'So can I trust you with that? And obviously you'll be a bridesmaid too, duh. Does that sound okay to—'

'Are you kidding? Obviously that's okay! More than okay. I'd be so honoured.' My voice is high-pitched and I'm rambling, but I don't care. 'It really means a lot that you'd think to ask me.' I'm grateful to the battering wind for hiding the real reason for my watery eyes.

Her shoulders drop in relief and she gives my hand a squeeze. 'I was worried you might not want to. But I should have known I could count on you.'

She tells me what they've got planned so far; ideas for the colour scheme, the venues they've arranged to view, the ongoing debate between traditional fruit cake and something more interesting. As she speaks, she gets increasingly animated, hands flapping and gesticulating. Not for the first time this evening, I find myself without much to contribute to the conversation, but that's okay. This is the norm; Tash full of big ideas, my job to smile and nod along.

It's only when her phone illuminates, with a ping that pierces through the harsh wind, that she comes to an abrupt stop. She looks slightly embarrassed at the interruption demanding her attention.

'Sorry,' she says and taps in her passcode – the same as always, her date of birth. 'James is with my family. I'd better go and save him from yet another game of Monopoly.' She rubs her bare knees again before pressing her hands into them to raise herself to her feet. 'You coming?' she asks.

'I'm going to stay here for a bit,' I tell her, but rise to join her. There's a slight pause, almost imperceptible but I know we're both conscious of it. She takes a step to close the gap between us and we hug. It's brief, but comes as a welcome relief. As she steps away, it feels as though part of my heart goes with her, residue sticking to her stylish duffle coat and pulling out like the strings of cheese between two halves of a toastie. She folds her arms around herself and looks out over the water, the lights of the city reflecting in her eyes.

'It's dead funny, seeing it from here.' Her voice is softer, harder to catch over the wind, almost as though she's talking to herself. 'It looks so much better than when you're in it. And from over there –' she jerks her head at the dark river '– you can see this. Which sounds shit, but it's actually nice, being able to see home.'

We stand for a moment; she's looking out, I'm looking at her. And then she clears her throat and turns to smile at me.

'Don't stay out here too long. And text me when you get in. Merry Christmas, yeah?'

'Merry Christmas,' I say. For a moment, it looks as though she's going to speak again, but instead she turns and heads off down the prom. I sit back down on the bench, right in the middle. I can feel the cold of the damp wood through my jeans, between the two warm patches we've made. I turn to watch her retreating figure, battling to walk in a straight line as the wind lashes a mist of water up from the Mersey.

'she knows
me too
well...'

OLD FRIENDS

AIRPORTS

JONATHA KOTTLER

I am thinking of all the times we have met in airports, when one of us has moved away. I picked you up in the Sacramento airport where I'd moved when I turned thirty. They have a huge sculpture made of plexiglass suitcases all piled on each other – airport art. We went to a smoothie bar and you had a shake with extra peanut butter because you were pregnant and craving protein. I was happy to be with you again – you being pregnant made us talk about when we sat together over in graduate school. We were supposed to be discussing *Marat/Sade* to prepare for class but instead our eyes were drawn to each baby that went past in a stroller or mama's arms along that busy street. We looked at their little feet. Their curly hair. What would ours look like if we each ran home and made a baby today with our partners and then they could play together and we could discuss *Marat/Sade* while our babies were playing.

But no. In Sacramento my son was four and your baby was a

tiny blip who wouldn't ever get to join us. And I was broken hearted because it happened when I was far away and couldn't help you.

And, then, a year later, I met you halfway between our two homes – at the airport in Phoenix where you, almost too pregnant to be allowed to fly, came down the concourse beaming, walking in that gorgeous, ridiculous way we all walk when expecting. We had dinner and walked around the mall, and I bought my son a Superman toy.

I moved back after that, and there were only car rides for a time. Trips to the aquarium with our boys and weekend getaways.

When you moved back to the east coast to take care of elderly parents, half of my heart went along in the boxes. I flew to the airport in Hartford (I'd brought a raincoat for some reason). Bradley airport was being remodeled and the long empty corridors had flickering fluorescent lights and I thought I would walk forever through a zombie-movie set and never find you. But your smile was there at the carousel where we waited for my bag to chug along (the only survivors of the zombie attack). Dinner at the Japanese restaurant, chicken and sushi in black lacquered boxes and the green tea flowed as if it was trying to keep up with the words as we bridged the distance by talking – your life my life my mother your in-laws the funeral, each sip and bite bringing us back to each other.

I picked you up in Albuquerque when I was moving, in my cute little Mini, tossing your suitcase in the back and driving what we called our 'farewell tour.' Each of us no longer in the place where we met, where our friendship was made, where I bound you to me with a hoop of steel. We drove by the place where we had *café au lait* and baby lust, and past the aquarium where our boys played and where we drank tea and dreamed of traveling to Paris. And you helped me pack up my life.

At Schipol airport in Amsterdam, we rode along on a train, side by side, your hand, real, flesh, making me feel stronger. Your visit shone in the darkness of my depression, my regret for giving up what I had for a failed adventure. You tried, bringing me an *Oprah Magazine* in your luggage and looking at every sight to show me how it could be beautiful through your eyes.

A few months ago I picked you up in Glasgow. I took a bus and then a train and then an airport shuttle, and I missed the ease of parking my car in the short-term lot. You came out of the doors from having your papers checked and it was as if the grey skies knew to clear. We sat together, cheek by jowl, on airport shuttle and train and bus, looking at my first article published in a newspaper on that very day.

Sometimes, when I am on a train alone, I see two old ladies with practical old lady haircuts and sensible shoes, leaning on the handles of their luggage and waiting for the train to take them somewhere, maybe to the airport, and I think of you and me and all the planes we have taken to each other and I know that will be us (but please don't let me do that to my hair – that sensible mannish old-lady haircut – promise me!). It will be us, taking to the air forever.

HERE IS WHAT
I MEANT WHEN
I SAID THAT

FRANCESCA RAINE

I love you. Do you remember the day
we spent with a beetle, rescuing
it from the middle of your parent's driveway, building
a home in the bushes from twigs and leaves? Your mum calling
us inside for lunch, then, after, it was gone.

Or our blue-checked summer dresses hitching
up around our waists, as we were rolling, laughing,
down the hill in the school field? Our classmates saying
we were too old for that, and the world already moving
around us, too fast.

The first trip into town on our own, riding
the bus like a horse-drawn carriage, bags bursting
with Tammy Girl t-shirts and cheeks aching.

Wiping away the sugar that was caking
your lips with the corner of my sleeve.

The sun-baked summer we all turned sixteen, floating
between the park and your parents' back garden, hiding
Smirnoff Ice we'd begged from your brother; talking,
with the sky darkening above us
and the night stretching out before us
of all the people we were going to be.

Midnight phone calls, walking
home from parties in another town, reassuring
voices at the end of the line. Miles turning
to minutes; whispers as we were creeping
up stairs a quick 'good night'
as the sun rose and dawn broke
bright and the milkman pulled up outside.

Hours spent in your nan's old car, driving
(just because we could) down country lanes and motorways,
    singing
along to songs we'd loved six years before, feeling
eighty miles-an-hour and limitless. Racing
home to say we'd been nowhere all day.

Outside bad nightclubs, crouching
on stone steps in cobbled streets, confessing
secrets to be discussed, later,
tomorrow, there's always time,
                        always time.

Flying visits, snatched phone calls, our twenties roaring
past, bad signal freezing your face on the screen, talk turning
to jobs and homes and deaths
and births. The future. The past.

City breaks and country walks and supermarket wine under
    the stars;
God and the universe and us, holding
hands between our camping chairs.

Here is what I mean when I say that I love you:
Look at all these patches of time that we have stitched
Together. Look at the boundless quilt
that we have made.

HER NAME
WAS FORTE

ALEXANDRA BURTON

It was a Thursday afternoon when I set off to board the ferry, bags packed into the same car your mum used to drive when we were teenagers. This was my life, now: all the possessions I could fit into a two-door Peugeot, nostalgic music on the stereo, and the country I'd lived in for twenty-six years in the rearview. I left everything else behind. My job. My family. Him.

In a grand gesture of farewell, I bought a packet of cigarettes from a petrol station near the house I'd just left empty. My thumb fumbled on the lighter for a few seconds, clumsy movements failing to produce a flame. I persevered. I needed the symbolism, the exorcism of whoever I had been. Click. Click. Whoosh.

I blew smoke into the wind all the way to Liverpool, watching cancerous ghosts billow and float and disappear.

*

I have never seen eyebrows raise more quickly than when I declared I was moving abroad to be with you, or heard so many whispers of hidden romantic agendas, like it's madness if it's platonic. Traverse the globe after just two months of passionate fucking and it's a whirl-wind romance, but pack your bags for a fourteen-year friendship and you can hear the pity in their speculation. It wasn't just for you, of course, but you were the North my internal compass pointed me towards. Back then, I needed you more than you ever needed me. The universe was pushing me so firmly towards a new start that I swear sometimes when I dawdled I could feel a hand at my back.

We lived together in a flat just outside the city, an ugly yellow building with carpeted stairs run threadbare and smeared with the grey remnants of old chewing gum. On that Saturday, we hauled my overstuffed suitcases up four flights because a sign on the lift deemed it 'Temporarily Out of Order', and I felt in my stomach the same giddiness that accompanies buoyant pre-holiday mornings. I couldn't smell the fish-curry scent escaping under the door of flat seven – I smelled coconut oil and factor 50 and fresh sea air.

My bags dominated the floor space of the box bedroom I'd get to call mine, and the walls, painted an aggressive pink, had a shrink-ing effect so drastic I wondered whether I'd have to curl myself into it like a hedgehog in hibernation.

'I've cleared you space in my wardrobe,' you said in a hurry as I appraised the room, 'and I'll buy you storage for the living room, I promise.' A pause. A smile. 'But only if you agree we can repaint those fucking walls.'

'It won't be like the movies,' someone warned me.

'It could ruin your friendship,' said another.

My darling, we stuck up our middle fingers at them all. Together, we spread ourselves until no corner of the place offered any doubt as to who lived there. It was a haven of wayward plants and thrift-store art and the paraphernalia of new hobbies, passionately loved yet quickly forgotten. We tore up the scuffed laminate and lay floor-boards, and in the evenings we would lie on a big old rug and write: me, poetry, and you, the children's book you spoke so animatedly about. This – you, words, our little sanctuary – was the tonic I needed, and we had never been closer.

I prepared us breakfast each morning, stirring sugar into coffee and buttering toast. You had a flimsy coffee maker that whirred and chugged, and sometimes the noise of it would summon you into the kitchen, sliding half-awake into a seat at the kitchen table. I always made your coffee in the same oversized mug that you could wrap your hands around, palms hidden beneath an enormous sweatshirt. In the daytime you were so loud and bright, but mornings painted you pastel-hued *piano*, all pale skin and gentle words. It was the only time I ever played the 'big sister' role, when you were unguarded and youthful in your softness.

Two weeks after moving in, I'd got cocky. I'd left the house without charging my phone and, when it had given up the ghost during the lull of mid afternoon, I decided I knew the city's bus routes well enough to make an educated guess. Take a left at the monument, I remembered, yet not as far as the spire. That day had been a Good Day, and I was encouraged by a fog of optimism.

When I noticed the streets that scrolled past the window housed buildings I didn't quite recognise, I was certain it was because I usually spent each journey with my neck craned over my phone. As the journey progressed, however, I realised I hadn't recognised a single landmark since I'd left the city half an hour earlier. The voice of concern in the back of my head made itself known. This wasn't a feasible consequence of inattention: I was simply on the wrong bus.

I was in a new city with a dead phone and no cash, and no way to tell where I stood in relation to where I needed to be.

I know this wouldn't have phased you. You, with your charming mix of confidence and hilarious self-deprecation – you would have sidled over to a fellow passenger and begged use of their phone, and they would have said yes because something in your eyes or voice left no other option. Or, you would have strutted up to the driver of the return bus and owned your idiocy, extracting sympathy and laughter. Your journey would have been paid for in charisma alone.

We were not the same, you and I. Your easy charm may as well have been a foreign tongue for all the sense it made to me. Instead, shame and anxiety robbed me of my words. I didn't want to ask for help, to out myself as a silly lost English girl. My brand of self-deprecation was merely pitiable, and my confidence nonexistent. Instead, I wandered the unfamiliar streets in silence until I found somewhere to withdraw cash, bought something I didn't need to break the note. I exchanged no more than three words with anybody.

When I finally made it back to the flat, over an hour later than usual, you poured me a glass of wine and we laughed together at my misadventures. My optimism. My acute awkwardness as a perpetual handicap. Here, in the safety of our four walls, the whole event was a distant and bizarre memory.

'Someone would have helped you out, for sure,' you said.

I agreed: yes, they would have, and suddenly I couldn't comprehend why I hadn't asked for help. But my voice was never as clear as when I was with you. You loosened my tongue; gave me permission to speak when fear would otherwise have silenced me. Your presence bathed me in an easy confidence that allowed me to play dress-up with self-belief. I marvelled at how you could always lend me so much strength whilst still keeping plenty for yourself.

Here, everything had the disconcerting quality of being both comfortingly familiar yet still so foreign, and you were the warm glow in the dark that helped me find my way home.

We made space for dating, but it sat somewhere on the periphery of our life together. The sting of a bad date was eased by the knowledge that we would return home to the other, where love waited unconditionally with a pithy joke or a shoulder to cry on. Neither of us needed romantic interest to feel complete, the way we used to when we were separated by an ocean and living with semi-hostile strangers. Our codependencies were reserved for one another; relationships were nice-to-haves, but we were untethered from compulsive seeking.

During the spring, you dated an Irish girl with a curly bob and a tattoo of Canada on her right wrist. She lived there for a while, you said, and you were enamoured with her in part because you wanted to live there too. You were a romantic; each new person was deposited neatly into an imagined new chapter of your life, and during your time together you would tell me increasingly detailed stories of transatlantic plans. A studio flat in Toronto. Stepping neatly into a new animation job whilst she taught English. Eventually, buying a house with a yard so you could adopt a dog and turn the basement into a home cinema.

After four months, you came home and told me she was moving to Thailand.

'Fuck, man. Why does everyone I like move away?'

It was true. There was the university boyfriend who moved to Germany before promptly breaking your heart; the almost-girlfriend who relocated to China for work; the live-in boyfriend who returned to Australia and asked you to postpone joining him, explaining, 'I just want to see whether I miss you'.

But you only liked her, after all: you didn't love her. I know this, because you didn't once cry. You drained a bottle of gin over the course of a weekend and theatrically bemoaned your terrible luck – but you didn't cry.

I offered up a fake proposal to you every time a man disappointed me, yet the truth is you were never second best. You were my first choice frowned upon by a society that says romance conquers all. We could raise children together, I said, and I meant it. I knew we'd make a better team than anybody I'd ever taken home to meet my parents. My parents loved you like a second daughter; it was already perfect. All we needed was to swallow our own discomfort at transgressing social boundaries, which stuck in our throats like a lozenge designed to return us to our voice.

In the beginning, the scales of need tipped towards me. I needed you to help me build a life: to find a job and navigate the public transport system and learn how to convert the currency in my head so I knew what 'too expensive' looked like.

Then one morning, you emerged from the shower wearing your pink towel and a look in your eyes like your world had been upended. They were swollen red and I remember thinking dumbly, perhaps it's shampoo, please let it be shampoo because you so rarely cried, but then you said, 'I've found…' and I could hear the blood rushing in my ears. I remember how you wordlessly took my fingers and pressed them against your skin. I hoped our senses were broken, neurons firing where they shouldn't, creating something imaginary that only we could feel.

I hoped as I made the call, my calm voice a distant stranger's. I hoped as we sat in the waiting room with its aggressive fluorescent lights making us ghastly. I continued hoping all the way into the doctor's office, your white knuckles alternating with mine; carried on hoping until I saw her face as she touched your flesh with gloved hands. It was fleeting – a micro expression of concern and pity – but in that split second I saw pallbearers, white lilies. Even in the absence of a diagnosis, the scales lurched towards you and my hope shattered to the ground.

I offered you words of comfort but I'm not sure I ever believed them. Perhaps, cursed by hindsight, my recollection is tinged with a grey pessimism. Or perhaps I weighed it logically; a potent combination of genetics, and the size of the thing, and the urgency with which you were summoned to the hospital to visit a grave consultant who pointed to black-and-white images and explained medical terms I frantically scribbled in my journal.

Still, I wanted to be proven wrong. I wanted my lack of hope to be a symptom of excessive caution, not a gut feeling grounded in reality. I wanted this to be a near miss we reflected on years down the line, sharing a relieved glance laden with the gravity of 'imagine if'. I was happy to give it the respect it deserved, to allow the momentary spike of fear to propel my life in some meaningful direction – as long as you were safe.

'Do you know what I hate about you?' you once asked, legs draped over mine as we deconstructed another unfortunate date. 'You're always fucking right. I hate it.'

This time I was. And my darling, I hated it too.

I held your hand as you telephoned your mum, and in the following days I spoke to her whilst you slept, making plans to return you like something I'd borrowed and held onto for too long. This was bigger than us. We had been a team, but this was an insurmountable ridge for which our collective years had not equipped us. We had encountered something that demanded more than existed within our cocoon of unconventional sisterly love and the smell of summer holidays. In the face of bleak reality, the life we had been living felt frivolous.

'You should stay,' you insisted as I assembled cardboard boxes on the living room floor. 'Don't uproot yourself for me.'

What I didn't say, couldn't say, was that you were my roots. You were the reason I was here, miles away from anything else I knew. Everything I was, and everything I had been since we met more than fourteen years ago, was knotted inextricably with the person you had grown to be.

I had built a life there, but without you I would rattle around in the shell of something that once was. Whatever I had acquired as a result – furniture, friendships, a job – now felt like incomprehensible footnotes, floating untethered and belonging to nothing at all.

So I followed you home, held your hand through tangles of tubes and tag-teamed shifts on a camp bed in your hospital room. I became your strength despite my own waning hope, because you needed someone to keep believing when you couldn't. We made plans to move to Toronto together when it was all over. I bought guidebooks and mentally furnished us with a wardrobe of snow boots and down coats, and when you complained about seeing the same four walls every day we'd look at photographs of national parks and imagine the cool air on our faces.

More and more, I saw the pale, softly spoken version of you that was previously reserved only for those grey city mornings. I would visit in the evening and there you were, lips cracked and eyes half-closed, and I had to overcome the sudden urge to shake you viciously into full consciousness. Where was my technicolour soulmate? Why was the world draining you away? I wanted to throw myself to the ground and pound my fists with the injustice of it all, as though my pitiful tremors could shake the universe into righting itself.

I wasn't accustomed to playing the role of the courageous or resilient. My timing was off and often I remembered too late what I ought to say. I wanted to look to you for guidance but for the first time you were trailing behind me, gripping my shoulder with your eyes closed. There was nobody to show me the way, and I felt persistently aware that I could be guiding us both into an abyss.

As time passed, you began to tell macabre jokes that would later repeat on a loop in my head whilst I sobbed in the sterile privacy of the hospital bathroom. With each quip, you held my gaze with two opposing demands.

The first said: don't you dare challenge me, I'm dying.

The second said: please, tell me I've got it all wrong. Tell me I'm not dying.

I didn't know which gauntlet to pick up, so often I said nothing. Out of view, I dug my fingernails into my skin and later I would leave with a fresh set of half-moon tattoos.

I followed you to treatment after treatment, to appointments with surgeons and kindly nurses who told us stories of their own best friends. I followed you everywhere until suddenly I couldn't follow you any more.

Sometimes I wake before the sun rises and sob in desperate longing for just one more day, one more morning waking up somewhere you might be.

On those days, I crawl out of bed and tiptoe to a kitchen you'll never visit, with a table you'll never sit at in your enormous sweatshirt. I butter toast. I stir your sugar and mine into a single mug of coffee. There are always grains in the last sickly mouthful, and in twelve months' time I will have holes in my smile like stars winking out of the night sky that will pay homage to you.

'*I thought we were friends...*'

FAKE FRIENDS

VIGNETTES OF YOU AND ME

CHLOE TOMLINSON

I.

This is how it begins. Hyde Park, Leeds, 2013, sometime in the middle of the night. Someone has been banging on the door downstairs and now I lie there awake, heart thumping dread. You appear in the doorway of my bedroom, a silhouette at first. But then a cloud moves and in the moonlight I can see you clearly. You are wearing an Australian cork hat, tipped forward, the corks dangling down and obscuring your face. One of my housemates must have let you in. Before going to bed I had greased coconut oil into my hair and wrapped an orange Sainsbury's bag around it to stop it from getting on the pillow, a plastic durag tied with an elastic band. On my face is an avocado face mask; avocado slime really, overripe and brown, mushed with Manuka honey. *'We aren't having sex,'* I say icily. We lie side by side in my bed, silent apart from the plastic bag crinkling against the pillow whenever I move my head slightly.

2.

Something changes. When you turned up at my house that time, I got out of bed early and asked L, with affected weariness, whether she still wanted to go to the library. Standing outside, smoking our cigarettes languorously, I said again and again, '*I think I've slept with a freak.*' No man had ever chased me like that; you were so open with it, it was off-putting. I focused on things about you that might explain it, like your violet eye bags, like the fact you could not grow a beard and your chest was smooth and pink. But then, something shifted, though I cannot remember what now, or when.

3.

You roll the red carpet out for me, keep rolling it out, like velvet, both of us like velvet. Salty, you say, like the sea. My pleasure comes from knowing that I satisfy you and I wonder briefly if your pleasure is from the same place, from the sense that you are there only to serve my wet lust. But I don't like the thought of this. Instead I think of myself, of how I am soft and ripe and easily bruised. When I am with you I am like a peach, full and wet, spilling out of my skin, pouring out of myself.

4.

One morning when I wake up my neck is purple with your love. Because I have a seminar to go to L gives me a silk scarf and I wind it gently around myself. I walk across Woodhouse Moor in the spitting rain and the bruising feels tender and swollen and delicious. '*Cunt,*' I say aloud, laughing, and it sounds like an incantation.

5.

We go out on a double date: you, I, L and her policeman-in-training. L and I walk ahead holding hands, a defiant laying out of priorities, a defence. We sigh dramatically and loudly lament the lack of sushi restaurants in Leeds, trying to make the point that we are Londoners-in-exile. It is that time of night: dusky twilight sky to match our eyeshadow and the feeling of our blood turning into wine, and in my Patsy Stone voice I am saying things like, '*it cannot be that difficult to find some simple sashimi in this godforsaken city,*' even though in London the only thing I ever ate was Morley's. I look back at you and you are smiling at the both of us.

6.

It is my housemate's birthday and there is a party for her at our house. You have to go to work and can only come round for a bit, and only that because I beg you to. When you arrive, I have no top on and am sticky from something spilt. Yesterday L and I found packets of neon blue shots in the pound shop in town, a dozen for 99p, and we bought four of them. Everybody is gathered downstairs in the kitchen listening to Daft Punk. '*Last summer I lost my anal virginity in a treehouse,*' I tell people, two packets of shots down and three sheets to the wind. '*We both did!*' '*Also,*' L shouts, '*also, everyone, these men, they spiked our drinks! We fell asleep in a booth and then we woke up in their treehouse and they were having sex with us and when we woke up again we were just randomly on the grass.*' We cackle conspiratorially at this, like it is the funniest thing we have ever heard said. There are some girls here I have never met who blink back at us politely, not knowing what to say. Afterwards you ask me directly, but I roll my eyes and bat you away. We demand a song, say we want to do a duet: the Tarzan-and-Jane song. It feels resonant.

7.

Later, I drag you into my bedroom and force myself onto you, and then I am getting sick on another bed upstairs and you are dithering in the doorway, needing to leave for your shift. There is an acidic pool the colour of strobe lights and little lumps of jelly splattered across the carpet. '*I love you Jane*,' I say to L, lifting my head limply from the pillow. '*I love you John*,' she says back. L is my best friend, and this is what we call each other, which sometimes makes other people uneasy. When I look up at the doorway again you have left.

8.

The next evening, when it is getting dark again, you text me to say that it is okay, that it doesn't matter. You come round to see how I am and hold me to you, dried out and disoriented, marooned together in this bed. I have had a shower but still I smell like a blister when you peel a week-old plaster off it.

9.

L and I go into town for a night out, down into a cellar that stinks of Red Bull and sweat, and I send you a series of vignette texts that you do not reply to, describing how we are being chased around the club by men who are trying alternately to shag and stab us. The tide has turned and now it is me getting a taxi to your house, uninvited, drunk. In the morning I wake up very early and feel regretful and ugly. My hair is matted, the texture of hay, and my breath rancid. I get out of bed and leave you lying there, sleeping serenely. I have flats in my bag and put them on, abandoning my heels which now, in the light of day, seem cheap and hideous. When I get home, I send you a text. *Sorry, went out for a cigarette and the door closed behind me, I couldn't get back in.* You reply a few hours later to tell me that it is one of those doors that doesn't lock behind you, you have to lock it with a key. After this, we do not speak for three days. I try to write my essay on Jean Rhys but everything she says makes me feel nauseous and my chest feels like a butter churn. I abandon it in favour of a two-woman pub crawl with L. We stay out until the sky is honey hued with sunrise. '*I need my shoes back,*' I say suddenly. '*I must get my shoes back.*' We bang on your door and you, bleary eyed, hand my scuffed heels to me, still saying nothing.

10.

When people say they drink a lot at university, I think: *you do not.* Tinkle tinkle of the ice in the bourbon, tinkle tinkle of the rain against the window, tinkle in my stomach, effervescence. I learn a new word at university: performative. When L and I drink together it is performative but also deeply true. I am my most realised self when with her, the sun beating down on us in a beer garden somewhere.

11.

In an attempt to distance myself from the woman I fear you think I am, I go to yoga and group meditation, but there is a cavern inside me and it is getting bigger and bigger the more I do not hear from you. Together, L and I bake a rose and pistachio cake, creamy and crumbling, with swirling buttery icing and velveteen petals around the edges. I post a photo of this cake online, caption it: *domestic goddess, much?* The day feels ominous. I have the mean reds, as Holly Golightly would say. And I am right to dread something, because that night you text me. *You are a mint girl,* you begin. (*Mint? Crème de fucking menthe?*) *But we are not right for each other.* Your words pop me like a pin and leave me deflated, a shrivelled balloon. The cake that I made for you sits untouched on the sideboard and turns slowly into an ugly Miss Havisham-esque piece of inedible shit. I will always hate the word mint.

12.

Sitting in our kitchen, days later, I smoke a Silk Cut and tell myself that this is all just a blip. '*Of course it is,*' says L. She bites her nails, and I order bell hooks and Audre Lorde books on Amazon. '*It's fine,*' L says. '*He'll be back.*' This is her constant refrain and I wrap myself in it like the sable-fur coat I once saw for sale on Portobello Road.

13.

I pour my alcohol down the sink and throw away all the bottles like someone in a film and go for a walk around the park. In my new cashmere scarf from the charity shop I feel wrapped up, cocooned, raw and elemental. People smile at me and I nod hello back. A woman with a whippet says, '*good morning!*' Walking in autumn in all its golden loveliness is like being drunk, high on the godly glow of the season. There is a part of me that is as wholesome as the trees. I draw strength from this sense of myself, but also sadness because you never saw it. You will think the newer version of me you see on Instagram is curated, which it sort of is, but sort of isn't.

14.

Two months later, on my birthday, Facebook tells me that you are 'in a relationship'. L says that she thought you looked like Uncle Fester all along. Tinder becomes a thing but all the good pubs in Leeds are tainted with memories of you, and I am not ready to surrender. Most days I am pinned to the bed with grief. L starts going out with girls from her course and I look at the photos they post. The girls are blonde, tanned, dewy skinned. I think of myself falling out of a car on the ring road, I think of the bark of the tree as it scraped against my skin, I think of all the strange things I have said to her friends visiting from London. Murky memories rising from the depths of me whenever I do not drink. In the waiting room at the doctor's, there is a poster which says *if you drink like a man, you might end up looking like one*, and underneath is a picture of a woman with hardened skin and clown makeup. '*Sertraline*,' says the doctor. '*Let's see how you get on with that.*'

15.

University finishes and I move to Liverpool. '*It is cheaper than London*,' I say when people ask me why. I pine for you. I am so ripe I sicken. A lot of people in this city sound like you. I get a temp job and the woman who sits next to me manically scrubs her desk and keyboard every morning, tutting and sighing at imaginary specks of dust. One day she asks me if I have a boyfriend. I want to wrest the wet wipe from her hands and rip it to shreds, throw the lime-stinking smithereens over her head like confetti.

16.

I meet L in London. A *reunion*, we call it, after months apart. We go to a café on the King's Road (her choice) and she tells me about a man she has met: a banker in his thirties. My skin is chalky white and my cheeks are sunken and my legs are mottled with bruises from dancing all night. The word rave sounds childish when I say it aloud. '*I just don't see myself ever doing MDMA again*,' says L over her eggs hollandaise, and it feels like a judgment. '*It was actually a sober rave*,' I say. It is a lie but over the next few months I will work hard to make it true.

17.

Sobriety: sometimes I am sparkling, hopeful. The next moment my eyes are leaden and my throat is dry with yearning. I go into the alcohol aisle and stare at what I cannot have. I post photos on Instagram of my milestones: three months, six months, a year.

18.

Then you send me a message asking if I fancy getting a drink. Yes, I say, yes, imagining us sitting together under the pink portentous Liverpudlian sky. When we meet, it is you, but also not you. You look the same but the air between us is not charged with lust. It is not charged with anything, not even nostalgia. I am shocked at the nothing that you are. '*I don't drink,*' I say. For ages I have imagined how it would feel saying these words to you, but you only shrug. You ask me if I am still friends with L. '*Not really,*' I say, as if the question is not loaded. You nod, sip your beer, stare into the froth of it as though transfixed. And then you say it. '*I'm guessing she never told you that she and I were sleeping together too, did she?*'

LOOKING BACK

ROSIE DASTGIR

You sat in the row ahead of me at school, with your killer instinct to get every sum right. You were always very good at maths, your work invariably neat, your pencil case immaculate, fat with crayons and rubbers, set squares and protractors, a pair of compasses stabbed into a cork. You always seemed to know what you were doing, unlike me. The pleated navy skirt, the combed blonde bob. You were the only girl in our class who could swim front crawl the full length of the pool at the age of seven, while the rest of us bobbed and shivered and clung to polystyrene floats at the edge.

When I meet up with you in Manhattan, thanks to a male friend we have in common, it's the end of the nineties and a decade since we've been in touch. You're an investment banker, which doesn't surprise me a bit, and – unlike me – you're very successful, a vice president. In fact you look like a president, in your pin-striped suit, whereas I look like a post-graduate, which amazingly is what I still am. You work in emerging markets, Latin America mainly, you explain, pausing for my reaction, which is slow, because finance is not something I know very much about.

The topic of turning thirty surfaces, and you admit that there is no one special in your life. I admit to an American boyfriend. You are impressed. I say I'm engaged. You are envious, though you already have a Green Card, which isn't the reason I'm getting married, I say. You congratulate me, and gaze into your drink, a Manhattan, and suck the maraschino cherry, withdrawing the cocktail stick as you swallow the shiny red sphere.

You like living in New York, even if you're not really keen on America as a whole. You claim not to miss England a bit, but I'm doubtful, because you are so English. You love netball, for example, and think that basketball is a really silly game. You were goal attack, I recall, and wore the royal-blue bib with the letters stitched on in white. Still, you could imagine throwing in your New York career for a life in the English countryside, making jam and raising a houseful of children. I laugh, not really believing it. Your round blue eyes fix me with a look: you'd like to meet more men. Can't I introduce you to some of my fiancé's male friends, you say, and I promise I'll try.

The next time we meet is at a bar, near your apartment on the Upper West Side. It is still warm, the tail end of September, and we sit outside, ordering a Mediterranean platter to share, a carafe of house red. You insist on paying for dinner. I accept. You offer me a place to stay. I accept that too. I've just been dumped by the fiancé, and I am shocked and shamed and unsure how much longer I can stay in the one-bedroom rental apartment on Columbus Avenue. I'm subletting it from his old college friend, Dana, who's getting married soon. Fortunately, it suits Dana that

I stay in the apartment for now – real-estate is the fulcrum of relationships in New York – at least till the wedding when her lease is up. The first of December is the date she's given for my departure, a deadline that's racing towards me as I sip my wine in the golden light.

Is it nice, Dana's apartment, you ask? And so I tell you about the rocking chair in the living space, the stiff cushions in shades of terracotta, the dusty sprays of dried flowers in vases dotted about on surfaces, and the Mexican-style rug. I mention the rickety pine table and the flimsy pine chairs that tip if you drape a coat over the back, and the piles of catalogues from mail-order companies that bank up in glossy slabs by the front door. But I don't tell you everything about staying in Dana's apartment. Like how I lie in her futon bed at night, the noise of the city thrumming the floorboards, and how I sift through her photo albums, dense volumes of past boyfriends on holidays in Rome and Paris and Tel Aviv. I don't mention to you that I've glimpsed her vaunted ambition in the ruthless lists she's left about the place, the avid forward planning. And I keep quiet too about borrowing Dana's coat, a camel hair by Calvin Klein, that I unsheathe carefully from its dry-cleaning bag in the hall closet, hoping she'll never know.

You and I finish everything on the platter, except for a pair of olives, bitter-black and shrivelled. It seems we're too polite, both of us, to disturb them. You generously reiterate your offer of a place to stay. You seem to want my company in a way you never did at school in the Venn diagram of our friendship set, the closed curves that circled and overlapped us, and kept us apart. I need to work some things out, I say, stalling, though privately desperate. Come whenever you need to, you tell me, not needing to finish the sentence. I feel an urge to hug you, but hold back. It's not something we ever did, you or I; a boundary never breached.

I juggle my time between finishing the graduation thesis, a short documentary film, and temping at Career Blazers. There isn't much work on offer, and sometimes I simply sit in the agency waiting for the call, while being paid to read a magazine. My cheque for the hours I've worked, or waited on standby, arrives a week later. I take a cab to your apartment one evening in the run up to Thanksgiving, just before New Yorkers funnel away to their families, and outsiders make alternative plans. You are thrilled, triumphant even, that we are both at loose ends. We dovetail at last. Two lonely single English girls in Manhattan. Then out of the blue, an invitation comes up. You are invited for Thanksgiving by a Colombian colleague and his Korean wife, you say, and I am invited along too. The more the merrier, the colleague says, and you seem elated that we're going together.

The couple's apartment, a condo, is in one of those high rises that sprang up on Roosevelt Island in the 1980s. We take the cable car, which you are excited about, having never done it before. You tend not to stray much east or west, sticking to your commute up and downtown. We don't speak during the ride, mesmerised by the muddy green East River unfolding thickly beneath us. The island rears up too quickly, before we've had a chance to orientate ourselves. Wordlessly, we disembark, our spirits dipping in the bleak windy walk to the apartment. But the host beams when we arrive and offers us jewel-bright cocktails in plastic cups. Smiling guests appear in clusters bearing Tupperware and foiled dishes prepared in advance, and the open plan space fills up, dense with a medley of accents. I can see that you are enjoying yourself, chatting tipsily to the husband who has topped up your drink with some electric blue concoction. I sip a Corona, with a wedge of lime jammed in the neck of the bottle. There are volleys of laughter from all sides of the room as the party warms up, enriched with the flow of new arrivals. I take up residence by the window, and sink into a modular sofa whose cuboid cushions drift so that I slip into the crevice. Luckily, I've made evening plans for us: I booked two tickets for the Charlie Mingus Big Band downtown. It wasn't my first choice, though I'm glad we have something else to do that night rather than be trapped here in Roosevelt Island. I wait for a gap in the conversation you're having with someone before I approach you. You flash me a look. We've only just arrived, you say, and cajole me into staying for the buffet; it doesn't take much. We eat and make an awkward early exit around 8pm. The hosts are crestfallen, though the wife displays a gracious smile as we escape before the party games get going.

We take a cab to the Village, and queue outside the club, filing in slowly with a tangled skein of foreign tourists and out-of-towners. The band plays brash but popular tunes that reverberate with dull familiarity in my chest. We don't say much to each other, hemmed into our separate worlds by the brassy sound. We stay for the first set, but the night is definitely flagging, and I feel your disappointment brim as you sit beside me, stroking the side of your glass. It's my fault, the way the evening has flatlined. Didn't I like the husband?, you ask me at one point, and when I say I don't know, you seem cross.

Your apartment is a tiny one bedroom with a galley kitchen, modern and sunny and tightly organised, just as I'd expect. You've done the bedroom really nicely, with its peacock-toned bed linen, the photos from home you've arranged, a framed map of Bedfordshire in the dark hall. I haven't been back since school, but I gaze at the contours of the landscape, remembering the sixth-form parties in village halls, and the time your older brother went off with my boyfriend. I keep quiet about this, and so do you. Every morning you rise at 6.30, and go swimming at a pool near your office in Wall Street before work, which begins at 8. You are still an excellent swimmer, though you've lately been plagued with ear infections and sore throats. While you get ready, pottering about in the kitchen, boiling water in a whistling kettle, eating cereal, I stay out of your way under the sleeping bag on the sofa, eking out the moments I can remain here. You have your routine now, and I respect it. I'm having a break-down, not that I know it until later. I've placed some of my clothes in your closet next to the bathroom. Folded shirts, a skirt, a few pairs of shoes, a jacket or two. You are surprised that I've made myself so at home, but you don't seem put out, just amused.

The uncertain temping regime is exhausting; cycles of hope and disappointment when no work materialises, followed by dread and relief when the agency calls and sends me on an assignment. Consequently, I don't feel like doing much in the evenings. The idea of us girls going out and about in the city does not appeal to me. You discover this gradually, when everything you suggest – a Mambo club in Chelsea, an east Village joint on Avenue A – I reject. I know you are disappointed that you never met my fiancé when we were together, or any of his male friends. Were they nice, his friends, you ask me? Some of them, I say, and you seem miffed. My thesis is my excuse for staying in most nights, but eventually it is finished, fine cut, sound edited. You begin coming home much later in the evenings, and we never eat dinner together, or breakfast, except after that all-nighter you pulled at the office. I don't ask you about the deal, and you don't try to explain, but we eat a bowl of Cheerios together, and sip some acrid coffee you brew. I miss English tea bags, I say, and you hint I should get out more.

I will be gone in January, back to England, I tell you, when you call me out of the blue at the offices of *Glamour* magazine where I'm working in Midtown. My student visa has finally run out, and there's no Green Card in the offing. I hear you breathe, and then a long silence, which makes me ask if you are OK. You are, you begin haltingly, but there's something. Sorry, I say, and my heart thuds in fear. You need your space, you say. I'll have to move. Nothing personal, you say, and I understand completely. A wave of heat rushes up my neck to meet the glow that blooms my cheeks. It strikes me that I shouldn't have set out my toiletries in your compact bathroom, with its precious few surfaces. I push away a memory of you aged seven, unzipping your pencil case, its artillery of writing tools at the ready. Don't worry, I say quickly, I'll be gone by this weekend.

Snow drifts outside the pre-war building on 116th, where the cab has dropped me. A janitor clears the sidewalk, scraping wet oblongs ready to receive more flurries spiralling down only to be removed by the shovel; the repetition comforting to watch. I squeeze past with my suitcases, and go up to the seventh floor in a creaky elevator.

Feeling my way along a windowless corridor I find the door to the studio sublet from a friend of a friend, and fumble with various keyholes punched in the reinforced metal door. I am struck by the smell of old bedding when I finally get inside to find that a huge floral sofa from Macy's hogs the space. My unyielding new room mate. It's too big for the two of us, but let's see who'll prevail. I tackle the plastic sheeting. This is where I will sleep for the coming weeks, inhaling the weave of upholstery as my cheek presses into the swirling cushions. The apartment is musty with the accretions of past lives, and I open the door to let the icy air circulate. The corridor has that old New York smell; cherry air freshener masking something else.

This time, I do not unpack. I stow my things in the cheap black suitcases that were a parting gift from my father before I left England for New York. The zips are shot, straining to contain my belongings. I have my ticket home, flimsy pages of inky red that stain my fingertips whenever I check them, which I do, repeatedly. I am counting down the days.

In the dead time between Christmas and New Year, I catch a glimpse of you outside Grand Central Station. Dusk, and the light is fading, but I am sure I recognize that blonde hair against your dark plaid coat. You are getting out of a black town car with a man who appears to be the husband from the Thanksgiving dinner on Roosevelt Island. I assume it's business, until you kiss him, disappearing behind a blur of yellow cabs, as he folds you into an embrace. I remember your words that day when you said how you needed your space, the self-assurance in your bid to evict me, and I walk into the wind tunnel barreling along 42nd Street without looking back.

Two decades slip past before you poke me on Facebook. Is it me? You can't tell, because I've changed so much. I check my reflection on screen, but don't confirm either way. You saw my book at Christmas in your local bookshop in Westchester where you now live with your husband of twenty years. You traded in banking for a life in the suburbs raising athletic and brilliant daughters. How funny to recognize our old school in print! And was that really you, the blonde swimming champion? I ignore your request to be friends, though not before I've peeked at the photos of you and Fabio by the pool at the Larchmont Country Club. My settings don't allow you to look back at me.

*'tell me
what's
wrong...'*

WOMEN
SUPPORTING
WOMEN

SELKIE

REBECCA COONEY

I keep the slivers of her self-esteem in a jar on the
    bathroom shelf.
I keep finding them around the house –
between the cushions on the sofa,
clogging the kitchen plughole,
scattered on her bedroom floor with her knickers.
She looks at me like she thinks I am collecting her toenails,
(intrusive, and a little disgusting),
but I cannot shake the feeling she will want them one day.

Silver and translucent,
there are more of them every time he comes around.
One day I come in to find the living room
iridescent.
The only dark corner is where she sits, dull and raw.

He is flaying her alive.
He jiggles the folds of her belly
made only by her position on the couch.
'What's this?' he asks. He is smiling,
but his fingers are teasing away another shimmering shred.
There is nothing of her and still he wants her to be less.
I glare at him, until he, guilty, notices and tries to put it back.

There is an ocean in her eyes, but the tide is going out.
She believes any port in a storm
(better to take this chance to dance than be cast adrift)
and I believe no dance is worth a damn
if it will cost you your skin.

When she moves in with him I fold the slivers from the
    overflowing jar
as best I can and put them in her suitcase
in the hope that one day, when her exposed soul is cold
she will mistake them for a cardigan, and put them back on.
As her skin flakes, she flakes away from me.
We drift apart as she chooses this landlocked type of love.
She wonders why I hate him, and I wonder
why she gave me the stories of the things he has done
if she wanted me to like him.

When she has gone I take out her tales and examine them,
and see they too are shot through with silver.
Too late I realise she gave them to me for safekeeping
and I should have given them back,

made her look at them until she saw how naked she was
and reached for the bathroom shelf.

Instead, I knit them into chain mail,
wear her stories as my armour
take my own jar from under the bed and place it by the mirror,
and try to remember to tell friends and lovers who are
   passing through:
'Your arms are not worth an ocean,
and if you cannot help me to put these back on
you do not deserve to stay'.

Sometimes I dream of him, soaked to the skin in a flooding flat
rising seawater backing up the bathtub, escaping
   salt-clogging sinks

and her swimming in the deep,
shimmering.

THESE STREETS ARE NOT OUR OWN

KIMBERLY KAY

We have a rule. We never agreed to it aloud, it just happened. Like the way no one teaches you not to laugh at a funeral – you just sort of know how to act once you arrive.

We found out the news as we were making dinner in the out-of-shape kitchen of our East London flat share. By the next evening the rule was enforced.

Of the four of us who share the house, only the half of us with breasts had to take note that our routines would now be altered, our small conveniences stripped. The half whose bodies become prey past certain hours.

I burnt the yellow dahl I was making and used that as an excuse for my foul mood instead of yelling to the room that I'm tired of people with breasts having so many more rules to follow than those without.

I clocked Elin from across the room as she ate her dinner with the same silent rage we are so used to swallowing.

The tunnel at the bottom of the road has always been on our list. A certain badly lit bus stop. A certain late-night convenience-store worker who'd given out too many creepy compliments and whose fingertips would always linger a little too long on ours as he handed back our change.

We'd mapped our escape routes and marked down our hit lists. Known that we'd jump a particular bend in a section of the fence and into the duckweed-covered canal if we had to. Promised that if it was past sunset we'd take the twenty minute detour to avoid certain routes. Known that if *that* call ever came our suspect list was ready.

But tonight, the park across the village made the list.

I take my burnt legumes upstairs to my room to eat alone on my bed and watch *Dinner Dates*.

Half way through the second episode, Elin makes her way onto my bed.

Every time she does this it warms the nine-year-old version of me. The girl who read *Baby-sitters Club* or *Harriet the Spy* and pictured that this is how real sisters and friends act – unannounced, without schedules or invitations.

We watch the rest of the episode in silence.

'She was our age you know,' whispers Elin while strangers cook unappetising meals for each other.

I know. I feel selfish for comparing us, like it matters if she was like me or not.

'It was just before midnight. Fuck sake, there's so many people about then. So many street lights and traffic lights. How does it happen there, then?!'

I'm still silent. I take time to process, while Elin needs to form sentences.

We both know it could have been either one of us. That it *was* one of us. This young woman, every woman – bleeding into each other. We know none of us are safe until all of us are.

Elin falls asleep. As she starts snoring, I turn off the laptop and tuck her in before sneaking across the hallway to get a good night's sleep in her bed.

The next morning, Elin and I do our usual Saturday summer morning routine of walking the five kilometre loop of the park in our active wear that never sees sweat. Herds of Hackney's finest bodies circle around us, bouncing pectorals and jogging dads with strollers making us lose where we are in our conversation.

In the daylight, the park is a utopia of how London's hipster elite get to live. Frisbees fly like it's not a childhood game we should have outgrown. Vegan acrobats hang up their slacklines, yoga circles sip kombucha and topless men walk their grey-velvet French bulldogs.

Once, Elin came home from a walk and ran into my room announcing she had seen Orlando Bloom running topless with his dog in this park. I wanted to interrupt, ask her for evidence he was even in the country, let alone in the park next to our house. But I let it go, let her have this one. I asked her what he smelt like and she went into a level of detail that made me hope for everyone involved it was him.

I met Elin the day I moved into my first London house share. She owned seven pairs of dungarees and her thick wavy blonde hair that she rarely had to wash always managed to look like it had been blessed by sea salt – an uncommon look in murky London.

We'd probably not have found a way to be friends if London's extortionate rental prices didn't force us to get to know each other's most intimate habits. Elin will be mid conversation and if she notices a wet, sticky substance on a surface her curiosity will always win out and she'll dip her finger in and lick it. Whereas I compulsively run the tap anytime I go to the bathroom to reduce the chance that anyone might hear that I have bodily functions.

Elin is also the kind of woman who doesn't squirm at first-day period sex. Swears that any guy who's put off by a bit of blood isn't worth the time it takes to take off your pants. While I wince at the idea of making a drop of mess that can be pointed to and called mine.

Last year I accidentally wet myself more than a bit on a night out waiting in line for the ladies' toilet. Elin marched us to the front of the queue and washed my pants while I relieved myself of shame and what pee was left.

From all of this, I know that Elin will be the first to notice if I ever get into trouble. Not in the all-knowing psychic-sisterhood kind of way – but in the way that the women in your life note down your details. They notice things, save the specifics.

Elin will know what channels to check and when to send for help. She'll know the chance of me going more than four hours without checking Instagram is less likely than me being in someone's basement. My boyfriend, taking a dozen more hours to clock on, will find out when my mother has called him in a panic.

Half way through our loop, we walk past the bush where the papers say it happened.

I wonder how she is. Wonder if she knows that she is more than a passing news headline about another woman who was raped. That she is forcing us into formation – a silent, synchronised dance on our streets to make sure it doesn't happen again. That we are putting her in prayers that don't beg for a God to help but for systematic changes only humans can create.

The rule is as follows:

Tunnel bridge

Bus stop

Convenience store man

Park pathway

You *always* call.

Neither of us will ever feel it a burden. It's not. It's our small defence. Like keys in our fists – you know when it comes down to it your fingers will fumble and you'll have no fight, but it brings small power to your shaking hands.

'I'm at *that* bus stop,' you'll say. The rest is known.

We'll pick up conversations in the middle, as if we're half way through an hour long conversation. It won't last long, so the narrative never has to make sense.

The call always ends the same way.

'Let me know when you're back home.'

And I'll wait up until I hear the sound of her keys signalling her return home or her knuckles knocking on my door. Because even the space in between the danger zones is not yet our own.

FINDING OUT

SALLYANNE ROCK

For Jo

Love was not where we were led to believe –
not in that boy's eyes,
his nervous hands
nor his clumsy poetry

It wasn't in that double bed
the one-kneed gesture
nor the dressed-up promise,
all soft-focussed and soundtracked

Instead, here is love –
in late-night talks over empty glasses
in long, undemanding hugs

and joy in each other's successes

It's in the softness of voices that say,
from miles away,
I'm here if you need me
and mean it

and if we had known
would we have followed those boys
to fields and beaches and churches

or maybe just rested together, love?

CONTRIBUTORS

In July 2019, we held a six-week open-submissions period for pieces of original creative writing by women on the subject of female friendship. We were overwhelmed by the response, and after reading more than 100 submissions we chose the fifteen pieces you have read in this collection. *Let Me Know When You're Home* wouldn't exist without the words of the women below, and we are honoured to publish them.

Alexandra Burton | @alxndrabrtn

Alexandra Burton lives and works in the north of England. When she's not writing you'll find her on the yoga mat, at the climbing wall, or tackling her growing TBR pile.

Rebecca Cooney | @RebeccaKCooney

Rebecca Cooney is a journalist and performance poet living in South East London. She has performed at open-mic nights and slams across London, and is the Cambridge Regional Hammer & Tongue Runner-up Champion for 2018. She is also the producer and co-host of the Dead Darlings podcast, a monthly podcast dedicated to the spoken-word scene in London and beyond.

Rosie Dastgir | @rosiedastgir

Rosie Dastgir is a writer and novelist, born in England to a Pakistani father and an English mother. Her non-fiction writing has appeared in the *New York Times Magazine*, *Stella*, *Planet Mindful*, and *Prospect* and she has written and presented for BBC Radio 4. Her first novel, *A Small Fortune*, was published in the USA, UK and France. She lives in Hackney, London, with her husband and two daughters.

Alice Godliman | @AliceGodliman

Alice is a Manchester-based writer, poet and spoken-word performer from South London. She has performed around London and Manchester and will be joining *That's What She Said* at Edinburgh Fringe this summer. Her work is often confessional, dealing with themes of feminism, body image, and the women she has loved through the lens of mythology or superstition and has been published by Dear Damsels and in *Dear Movies*.

Jade Greene | @collectedthinks

Jade is a writer of scripts, stories and creative non-fiction. She writes largely for children, from feature films to short stories, but after starting a blog about miscarriage and infertility she is now developing a play on the subject to tackle the taboo and open up conversation. Her blog and other projects can be found at collectedthinks.com.

Kimberly Kay

Kimberly Kay is a writer who uses the power of words to mobilise the masses and empower minorities. Having worked with some of the largest campaigning and development organisations in the world, from Amnesty International and Change.org to Girl Effect, she knows first hand the real-world change that is made possible through the power of storytelling.

Jonatha Kottler | @jonathakottler

Jonatha Kottler is an American writer and educator from Albuquerque, NM, USA, who, until recently, was based in Scotland. Her work has appeared in *Nasty Women*, and in publications including the *Guardian*, *NY Magazine* and the anthology *Luminous: Defiant*. She has previously written the short pieces 'A Tribe of Writers' and 'Gravestones' for Dear Damsels. She works with the Lighthouse Writers Workshop and is completing her first novel.

Huma Qureshi | @huma_qureshi_uk

Huma Qureshi is an award-winning author and journalist. She writes for several national publications including the *Guardian* and the *Observer*. Her book, *In Spite of Oceans*, is a collection of short stories of love, loss and loneliness set to the tune of south-Asian family life. Huma blogs at Our Story Time.

Francesca Raine

Francesca Raine lives near Manchester, writes fiction and poetry, and is currently working on a novel. She likes to write about friendship and family relationships, particularly between women. She dreams of having a pet labrador and has not yet managed to get to grips with social media.

Sallyanne Rock

Sallyanne Rock works in telecoms but leads a secret life as a poet. Her work appears in various journals online and in print, including *Eye Flash* and *Finished Creatures*. She has worked as an assistant writer in a young writers' group with Writing West Midlands, and has recently begun facilitating workshops of her own.

Sara Sherwood | @sarasherwood

Sara Sherwood lives in Leeds. Her short story 'Likes' was Highly

Commended in the 2018 Bridport Prize, and her fiction has been published in all three Dear Damsels annuals. Sara also writes for *The Heroine Collective*, and produces the podcast Never Marry A Mitford.

Hannah Simpson | @hannahsimpsonwrites

Hannah Simpson is a writer of short fiction, originally from the Wirral and currently based in Manchester. When she's not writing, she can be found locking people in rooms and watching them solve puzzles to escape (for a job, not just for kicks), and spending a truly unhealthy amount of time scrolling through Instagram. She would really appreciate a follow.

E.V. Somerville | @evsomerville

E.V. Somerville is a spoken wordsmith, anthropologist, and mischief-maker from South East London. She has a passion for talking with strangers, making things, and exploring on foot. She has been writing non-fiction, short stories, poetry and snail mail since she could hold a pencil. She has performed her original spoken word at WOMAD, Means:Identity Festival Amsterdam, and even a disused police station in Deptford.

Chloe Tomlinson | @chloemariegenevieve

Chloe is from London but currently lives in Manchester. Her short story 'My Man, Leonard' was published in the *Dublin Review* in 2019. She loves reading, writing, and having long, lavender-infused baths. She is currently working on a short-story collection.

Hannah Wright | @hanjmwright

Hannah lives in Edinburgh and works both as a digital marketer and a trapeze teacher. She writes arts reviews for the *Wee Review* and was accepted on to the Scottish Review of Books' Emerging Critics scheme in 2018. Her creative writing has previously been published on Dear Damsels, the *Suffragette Stories* online anthology, *Silk & Smoke* and the *London Reader*.

THANK YOU

Let Me Know When You're Home would not have been possible without the people who supported our Kickstarter, helping us raise the funds needed to bring our first book to life. Friendship and connection is central to what we do at Dear Damsels, so in many ways this is a project that reflects our aims as a collective – while the crowdfunding of the publication is further proof of what women can achieve with the support of each other.

We'd also like to thank Anna Woodbine for her cover illustration, Marcus Chamberlain for his text design, and our project editor Kitty Stogdon for her support throughout the entire process.

Abi Fellows	Alice Slater	Amanda Reeves
Adeline Schmitt	Alice-May Purkiss	Amy Tunstall
Adil Ladha	Alicia	Annabelle Beugnet
Alex Barber	Alizee Chesnoy	Ariel
Alex Gorman	Amalia	Asta
Alice Chamberlain	Amanda Costigan	Barry Parsons

Becca

Becca Hone

Becca Steel

Bernadette Morabito

Blaise Donald

Bobby

Caitlyn Hunt

Carolyn Barth

Carrie Walsh

Cat Widdowson

Catherine Watson

Catherine Whiterow

Charlotte Crewe

Chloe Green

Chloe Hashemi

Christine Hanway

Christine Moorhouse

Clare Weze

Daisy Payling

Dan Chiniara

Dan Smith

Dan Smyth

Daphne van de Burgwal

David Hunt

Dawn Godliman

Debz Butler

Donna Tomlinson

Elena Trimarchi

Elizabeth Bavin

Elizabeth Lovatt

Ella Sinead Gordon

Ellen King

Ellen Warwick

Ellie Davidson

Ellie Wilson

Emily Langley

Emily Somerville

Emma Crouch

Emma Duddingstone

Emma Gannon

Emma Kenny

Emma Post

Emma Staples

Erika Norrie

Ernesto

eSpec Books

Esther Sparrow

Eve Mulcahy

Fari Da

Felicity Green

Francesca Pridding

Gab Stell

Gabrielle Turner

Gem Cowin

Gemma Seltzer

Grace Brown

Grace Safford

Han Mary

Hannah Bond

Hannah Jordan

Hannah Simpson

Hannah Watson

Hannah Wright

Haritha Gnanaratna

Hatti Whitman

Heather Kirkpatrick

Heidi Gardner

Helen Ainsley

Helen Kitchen

Helen Maria Arnold

Hilary Bell

Huma Qureshi

Imogen Battersby

IngeniousPrairieDog

Isu Jusi

Jaminx

Jan Greene

Janet Baxter

Jason Kottler

Jess Glaisher

Jess Jones

Jess Masterson

Jess Toft

Jill Furedy

Jo Kowalik

Jo Myler

Joanne Fisher

Jodie Manning

John Prebble

Jonathan Wilkinson

Jude de Bont

Julie Sherwood

Karis Gully

Kasia Bens

Kate Todd

Katie Hogan

Kelsey Griffiths

Kerstin Weinwurm

Kim Hobbs

Kim McGowan

Kimberly Kay

Kira Swales

Kitty Stogdon

Kitty Underhill

Kovacs Robert Daniel

Lara McGrath

Laura Colledge

Lauren Pinnington

Lea

Libby Earland

Lizzie Streeter

Lucy Hilton-Jones

Manon Bendahmane

Marci McCann

Marcus Chamberlain

Maria Moore

Marion Nicolas

Martin Keeling

Mary Young

Matilda Johnson

Maura Fertich

Meguey Baker

Melanie Ashford

Molly Cooper

Molly Tobias

Morag Wright

Morgan Witkowski

Morphine

Mrs B Emery

Myrtille

Nadia Henderson

Niamh Anderson

Nicole Boucher

Nitya Tripuraneni

Nnena Nwakodo

Nora Selmani

Olivia Bays

Olivia Sleet

Oyuntugs Luubaatar

Paula McGregor

Philippa K

Rachel Belward

Rachel Knott

Raphael

Raphael Kabo

Rebecca Jaramillo

Rebecca Peters

Rebecca Wilks

Rhia .

Ria Patel

Rosaleen Lynch

Rosie Siman Yakob

Saima Mir

Sally Ann

Sally Hamilton Williams

Sam Birch

Samantha Cullum

Samantha Graham

Sandra Paul

Sandy Bennett-Haber

Sara Adams

Sara Cox

Sara Owen

Sara Westrop

Sarah Briscoe

Sarah Garnham

Sarah Hardy

Sarah Rushbrooke

Sarah Tinsley

Scarlett Kefford

Sean Wilkinson

Seona Bell

Shara Bajurin

Sharon Parsons

Shaun

Shaun Carr

Shivani Khosla

Sonia James

Sophie Appleby

Sophie Douglas

Sue Barsby

Sue Kewely

Sue Simpson

Susan Shipley

Sweaty Betty

Tania

Tasha Turner

Teona Bonsu

Terri-Jane Dow

Thea S

Trevor Binyon

Victoria Clarke

Victoria Jones

Yellow Yeti Games

Yuling

Yvette Cooke

Zainab Kwaw-Swanzy

Zinzi Mangera-Lakew

dear damsels

your words | your stories | your collective

deardamsels.com

 deardamsels

 deardamsels

 deardamsels